Wes Schum, Amateur Radio's Unsung Hero

Dominic (Nick) Tusa

Jan-Carol Publishing, Inc
"every story needs a book"

Wes Schum, Amateur Radio's Unsung Hero
Dominic (Nick) Tusa

Published September 2021
Heirloom Editions
Imprint of Jan-Carol Publishing, Inc.

ISBN: 978-1-954978-18-8
Library of Congress Control Number: 2021945488

You may contact the publisher:
Jan-Carol Publishing, Inc.
PO Box 701
Johnson City, TN 37605
publisher@jancarolpublishing.com
www.jancarolpublishing.com

To the Schum family, who once welcomed a young, half-frozen stranger from Louisiana–improperly dressed for a frigid, snowy Chicago winter–with warm open arms.

Author's Note

It may come as a shock to you readers, but as a young lad I had zero interest in writing. NONE. Instead, I was captivated by the magic of Shortwave Radio—the ability to listen in to news and stories transmitted *without wires* from very faraway lands. To those aged 20 and younger, it must sound like us Baby Boomers had some prior residency in the Twilight Zone.

Yet in the early 1960s and with the backdrop of the Cuban Missile Crisis, us kids having clandestine access to Dad's Hallicrafters shortwave radio thought we had become the James Bonds of our time. In many a darkened room, like spies we quietly listened to Morse Code numbers transmissions or contemplated those strange Russian announcers from Radio Moscow, spinning their web of propaganda! Of course, we *were* spies of a sort...most of our friends were clueless of shortwave and its many hidden gems.

Those eerie sounds heard, and the distances travelled naturally lead to the fundamental questions that drive scientists and engineers of all stripes: How, what, and why? How does a human voice become a radio signal? How can radio travel thousands of miles without wires? What makes up a transmitter, receiver, and antenna? How can one squeeze more radio stations into an ever-smaller space?

By the age of ten, I wanted my own radio station...like those ham radio guys. So, I studied and passed a set of grueling tests (especially for a kid with then-limited math and science skills) and climbed the amateur radio licensing ladder. By high school, I instinctively knew what I wanted out of life—to design and build radios and electronic gadgets. I soon became aware of this young fellow in Chicago who had done what I had dreamt of. His name? Wes Schum.

In time I met Wes, first by mailed letters, then by telephone calls, and finally by an in-person visit to Chicago. He became my mentor and we had a friendship as close as father and son. He taught me how to be a successful engineer/entrepreneur. He encouraged me through his life's experiences to accept responsibility and to keep an open mind to learning. Like many of his generation, his future was greatly shaped by World War II. Many movies and books showcase the battles won and lost during that period and the sacrifices shouldered by America's service men and women, but little is said of the home front's war.

The important technologies such as RADAR, the Norden/Sperry bomb sight, the VT proximity fuse, code-breaking analog and embryonic digital computers (mechanical and electronic), and vast improvements in radio/telephone communications were borne in labs, workshops, and manufacturing facilities far removed from the front lines. People like Wes Schum and many thousands of others worked tirelessly throughout World War II to give the Allies the tools needed to win. And, once the war was concluded, those highly skilled people helped propel the United States into its most expansive period of technological prosperity of the 20th Century.

I expect this book will be largely read by "Boomer-era" amateur radio operators—particularly since I am one of you! Here, readers will learn about an important company, started by a husband and wife team as a basement operation, that brought exciting technology to a post-war market. Their success, though, did not come without costs and challenges—a key part of the book. Those sorts of real-world obstacles seldom get deserved attention in business-related self-help books...yet, it has been my experience where best-learned lessons are those precipitated by some degree of pain and failure (in the PC World sometimes known as *Unintended Consequences*).

In the end, I hope you Ham Radio operators enjoy this book, get soldering irons warmed up, and restore bits and pieces of our hobby's rich technical legacy. Yet, my hope is for Wes Schum's story to be passed down to *young people*—those who are just beginning to quantify their life's passion. I know Wes would be thrilled if just one young person was motivated to overcome fears of the unknown and pursue an engineering or manufacturing career path. Dreams can become reality, if one believes in themselves and seeks the sage advice of people who have been down those well-travelled roads. Take it from me...it works!

Foreword

By Bob Heil and Dr. R. Sullivan

Bob Heil, K9EID
Heil Sound, Ltd.

In the mid-1950s I had only been into amateur radio for a few months as K9EID on the 6 meter band. The second or so week I ran across the most distorted AM signal on my Hallicrafters SX99..."what was wrong with *THIS* guy?" I thought. The next few nights I heard it again (keep in mind, I'm just a budding new ham operator) so after fiddling around on my SX99 one night from all of that distorted noise–bingo, a voice popped out! Now, I started fine tuning things (I had no idea what all of the buttons on the SX99 did), but I tweaked the BFO and the voice was there.

I was most afraid to call the guy with the weird sounding signal, but I did. I was using my little Harvey Wells AM transmitter then. And he came back to me! When I heard that "K9EID this is K0DGE" I got really nervous, as I had only been on-air for a few weeks, but we began talking. Can you imagine guys in the mid-1950s on 6 meter hearing this new SSB noise on their primitive Gonset, Lafayette, etc. AM receivers?

That one chance radio contact for a very nervous kid started a long time relationship...Larry (all I knew him by at the time) invited me to stop by and visit sometime in St. Louis. I told him I came into St. Louis three to four times a week to do my duties playing the Wurlitzer at the Fox Theater. I had just turned 16. During one of my 3-hour waits while the movie played, I pulled up in front of his address....It was KMOX radio—Larry *Burrows* (finally, a last name!) was the chief engineer at this CBS affiliate station. He took me on a station tour and of course I was mesmerized by all of this.

Larry, it turns out, had built one of the first 6 meter SSB stations when virtually no one was using sideband on VHF bands. To generate his sideband signals, he modified a Wes Schum Central Electronics 10B exciter, built a 36 mc mixer-oscillator and 6 meter output coil to plug in. Bingo— he was there. I asked him that first meeting if he would build *ME* one of those rigs. Looking me straight in the eye, he said no, he couldn't do that, but he could *teach* me how. And he did.

OK—enter Wes Schum. Armed with a laundry list of needed parts from Larry, I was on a mission. I went up the street to Walter Ashe Radio, bought a 10B kit, blank chassis, Greenlee punches, 6U8A tube, ordered a 36 mc crystal, and I was on my way to a tremendous future. Building the 10B, I started reading all I could about the transmitter, Wes Schum, but never dreamed I would meet him. So, that first W9DYV meet in Jonesborough, Tennessee for me was extremely emotional and important. I wave the Wes Schum flag very, very often—reminding people that it was Wes, not Art Collins, who first brought commercial SSB to amateur radio, and he is a center piece in each of the presentations I've hosted at various ham radio meets.

When people ask, "Who is Wes Schum?" my response is always, "He was the college professor I never had." From him I learned about phasing, which has served me well in building a career in studio/concert sound and broadcast microphones. He inspired countless others. Without a doubt, Wes Schum is amateur radio's unsung hero. He helped pave the way for single sideband's widespread acceptance in our ranks. I miss you Wes...No, the entire amateur fraternity misses your design talents and your thoughtfulness of bringing new technology to our beloved amateur radio.

* * *

Dr. R. Sullivan; EE
Great Falls, VA

This is an important book! Single Side Band (SSB) communications was and is very important to radio communications. Nick Tusa's story of Wes Schum and his contribution to the acceptance of SSB lays out just what it took to build a company based on a new, unproven communications concept and ultimately provide affordable SSB transmitters to the amateur radio community.

Why is this important? Historically, amateur radio has been in the forefront of new ideas and has been responsible for setting many on the path to a career in Electrical Engineering. I'm no exception! Being able to 'play' with the newest ideas is a big part of our hobby. Wes Schum and his company Central Electronics provided just what was required; affordable SSB equipment to allow many hobbyists the chance to experiment; the mainstay of our hobby.

Reading Mr. Tusa's story about the life of Wes Schum surely will be inspirational. If only one reader goes on to a career in Electrical Engineering, Nick's book will have been worth all the effort he put into it.

Introduction

The development of any new, innovative product is always a risky proposition. Will the developer be able to craft a reliable product that furthers the art and spurs the imagination of others? Will those new and somewhat radical ideas receive a warm welcome, or ignite hostile passions of rejection? In short, will my glowing idea fly like an eagle or swim with the fishes? Developing anything new takes laser focus coupled with a strong desire to succeed at all costs, knowing heady obstacles and unforeseen challenges await.

Not everyone has the temperament, belief in their own abilities, or stamina to invent a new process or chart a course in an entirely new direction. The safe bet is to stick with the status quo; but without risk, from where comes reward? Breaking away from the pack is an oft-lonely road, lined with detractors and progress saboteurs each step of the way. You see, there is never a clear path to success. Some might call the impediments to progress *failure*.

Of course, nothing is truly a failure in the sense that each unexpected result brings with it a requirement for deeper understanding. Why did the expected result not occur? What did I not understand? Is my theory based on a solid foundation, or wishful thinking? Those special few who brush off setbacks in progress to continue seemingly unscathed have innate abilities to refocus, rationalize what is learned, adjust to new ways of approaching a solution, and find a new pathway home.

Winston Churchill often spoke of success and failure in this way: "Success consists of going from failure to failure without loss of enthusiasm. Success is never final. Failure is never fatal. It is the courage to continue that counts."

Those who lived through the Great Depression of the 1930s and the darkest years of a world at war felt the sting of what could be viewed as an unending string of failures. Economies crashed, banks failed, livelihoods were wiped out in an instant, and the world itself was engulfed in chaos. Many were paralyzed by fear. Some withdrew from family and friends, sadly into the fatal depths of despair. Others, unafraid of the unknown, fought their way free and charted new courses in Life.

Against that backdrop, our nation experienced unprecedented growth in technology throughout all disciplines of science and medicine, throughout World War II and the immediate post-war years. Advancements in electronics—the focus of this book—brought dramatic improvements in two-way communications technology, more rugged and reliable electronic components, and important electronics-based solutions that played key roles in winning the War. Where would Britain and the Allied Forces have been without the development of radar, the proximity (VT) fuse, reliable radio voice and telegraphy linkages, or code-breaking computers?

When one thinks of World War II, the normal focus is on battles won and lost, the strategies used by the military's field commanders, how in-field actions had to adapt to changing conditions, and the sheer ferocity of battle. The stress, hardships, fear, sacrifice, and anxiety shared by those on the front lines, at sea, and in the skies are difficult to comprehend, even viewed through the lens of 80 past years.

One thing is certain: The arsenal of war was forged by those on the home front. It was here that the needed ships, planes, vehicles, tools, and armaments were designed, perfected, and manufactured on a scale that has yet to be equaled anywhere in the world. It was people, the men and women coming of age in the early 20th century, who were tempered by hard times and the constant challenge of working tirelessly to build that arsenal from all but nothing—and in a scant five years. It was these resilient individuals who later rebuilt the world, invented new technology, and were open to sharing their hard-won knowledge with others.

This book is a view into the life of one of those people, although his story is one that shares resonance with a great many others who used their talents to help change the world. He put his all into the war effort, built a family, helped usher in an exciting new form of radio communications, and helped others achieve their dreams. In short, he was one who embodies the American spirit. I hope you enjoy his story, find yourself in these pages, and chart your own special course.

Chapter 1: Meet Wes Schum

It seems every neighborhood has one. It's easy to spot, because to many they're ugly, ungainly eyesores that can't possibly have any useful purpose. Why would anyone want one in their backyard, of all places?!

It's not a "land yacht" RV or an oversized sailboat, not a hot rod in some state of disrepair, sitting on cement blocks. Or even that leaf trap, money-pit, hole-in-the-ground called a swimming pool. No, of course I'm talking about a radio tower—and not just any radio tower, but a *ham radio* tower! One with all sorts of spidery pieces of aluminum and wires emanating from all angles.

Radio tower

Oddly enough, once one ham tower sprouts in a neighborhood backyard, like crab grass others soon follow. Not to mention what next happens to non-ham television receptions, intercoms, home alarms, and stereo systems—even garage door openers are in open season. Let's not forget the Internet; whatever is electrically wired becomes fair game for perceived ham radio interference.

Argh!

You see, amateur radio (also known as ham radio) is a hobby with roots reaching back to the earliest days of radio experimentation. In fact, theirs was the domain of electronics experimenters and hobbyists well before the radio's first commercial broadcast of Morse code, music, or human speech made its way into the public's mindset.

As it does even now, radio quickly captured minds and adventurous imaginations, mostly among young people (and those young of heart). It brought with it a sense of adventure, much like what the early explorers felt when unsteadily setting sail into the ocean's unknown. For the radio adventurer it becomes an invisible, unending set of challenges: What is that weak signal? How can I make it clearer? Can the other fellow hear me? What can I do to make my signal stronger? How is it possible to communicate ideas by radio? Can I send my own voice thousands of miles over the air? What can I do to make this even better than today?

The ham hobby grew from a small handful of people to one that now has over three million licensed radio amateurs, worldwide. More importantly, it is a hobby that has inspired many to become scientists, engineers, inventors, and technologists who later brought important realities to society in many forms: television, telecommunications, sound, motion pictures, and computerization, to name a few.

World War II brought an urgent need for electronics specialists and the ham radio community—comprised of seasoned professionals, hobbyists, and those new to electronics—did its part. The unprecedented and highly accelerated progress in electronics and wireless communications during WWII found a ready audience of business and industrial buyers in the post-war years. Of course, amateur radio benefited as well with a

Wes Schum

post-war flood of young men brimming with ideas and dreams of new products to make ham radio more fun, and society a better place.

Wesley R. Schum was one of those young men. Born in Chicago in 1921, his interest in radio began well before high school, having taken root in 1932. He later made his mark during the war years by heading an engineering team for a manufacturing company supplying important electronic devices, serving both the US Army and Navy.

Soon after V-J Day in 1945, Schum was drafted into the US Army to become a prisoner interrogator and counter-intelligence operative, destined for Korea. By January 1947, Schum's war was over and a new career path—one that provided equipment to help impaired children hear sounds and learn important language skills—had begun.

Ham operator in the 1930s

Schum's best-known work, though, circles back to his life-long attraction to amateur radio and his efforts to bring the then-new form of radio communications to ham radio enthusiasts: single sideband. Schum's Chicago-based company Central Electronics, formed in 1949 in his home's basement, played an important role in making single sideband (which some called SSSC) affordable for ham operators. His Central Electronics startup grew rapidly in the early 1950s and ultimately became a subsidiary of the important Zenith Radio Corporation.

Central Electronics—Zenith subsidiary

Knowing a thing or two about Wes Schum and his early formative years, it is clear the ingredients of success were ingrained early in life. Like Churchill suggests, success for Schum required a continuous infusion of confidence and courage. As you will come to know, this man was filled to the brim with both. What follows next is that important, beginning part of the Schum story, in his own words:

"I was born in Chicago on December 7th, 1921 at home. In the early 1920s my father, Leo Schum, owned a factory that made hand-rolled cigars. His business employed about 125 men and supplied cigars to taverns and stores all over Chicago. Prohibition was voted in and became the law of the land on January 17th, 1920, which meant Dad lost all his inventory and business consigned to the area's taverns. As time when on, the business shrunk as fewer establishments were opened to carrying his products. Thus, we moved from a steam-heated, comfortable home into a cramped, stove-heated residence with my mother's father.

"Grandpa Muench was a staunch German with a handlebar mustache that was snow white. He apparently liked me, because he showed me how to use and respect machinery. Grandpa had a shoe repair shop in his basement. In fact, just about everyone had a business of sorts in their basement!

"As Prohibition's noose tightened on local taverns, with most forced to shut down, Dad turned to his alternative profession: bootlegging. You see, my dad was born in a Tennessee town called Powell Station, near Knoxville. As a young man, he learned how to make alcohol from corn or sugar—a skill which became rather important later in his life and mine. So, when Prohibition set in, he eventually became a partner in a group that had a hidden-in-plain-sight still in Cicero, a suburb of Chicago.

"I was about five years old (year 1926), but even at that young age remember a row of deep old-fashioned bathtubs, each having vent hoods above, all connected through stove pipes to the chimney of the bungalow. From the outside, no one would ever know or suspect the secrets held inside. Dad's group bought big bags of sugar, wholesale, and transported them at night to avoid detection. Those bags looked enormous to me, but of course everything looks big to a 5-year-old!

"The alcohol would become bourbon, scotch, or gin by putting in some loosely-prescribed number of flavoring drops per gallon. It apparently made do—if one had leathery tastebuds and a vivid imagination! In some cases, so much so that they were willing to pay for it with diamond rings, as I later found out from Dad.

"Deliveries to customers along Lake Shore Drive were always done at night, for obvious reasons. Dad owned an auto that had a removable back seat where the gallon tins of liquor were hidden during delivery. I was along on one delivery occasion when the police stopped all cars and searched for the illegal booze. Dad said 'Wes, lay down across the back seat and pretend to be asleep. Do not open your eyes when they shine a flashlight on you.'

"It worked! They waved us on, and the delivery was made.

"I made many other midnights runs with Dad. One time, though, our luck looked to be running out. A cop at one road-block remembered the car, me on that back seat, and began putting two and two together. I could hear an argument brewing between Dad and the policeman, him wanting to move me off the back seat for a closer look and Dad arguing back that his son was tired and cranky. Immediately, I could visualize Dad being hauled off to jail, maybe to never see him again. I started sobbing uncontrollably.

"Dad, sensing an opportunity, railed back at the cop, yelling at him that he had awoken and scared his young son for no good reason. The policeman, thoroughly embarrassed by his heartless actions, waved us on. Once on the road again, the waterworks instantly stopped and we both broke out in side-splitting laughter! That night, though, spelled the end of my young, aspiring booze-running career, once Mom got wind of what happened.

"It was also about this time in my life when I had my first experience with electricity. I was very curious about those plates in the wall, and decided one night after dinner to see what would happen if I stuck my fork in one of the holes. *Ahhh*! I survived the experience with quite a scolding from Mom, and was off and running on my quest to find out what had happened to me and why.

"There was no time to waste being a kid in the 1920s. Everyone, young or old, worked to survive. Dad's alternative profession soon allowed us to move into a rented house that had a potbelly coal-burning stove in the dining room, which was supposed to heat the whole house. My job was to gather kindling wood to start the fire. I would bring home discarded empty wooden fruit boxes in my wagon from a local produce market. By this time, Prohibition had become wildly unpopular and speakeasies had sprouted up in the oddest of places...but then the banks suddenly closed in an instant. The stock market crashed, and the Great Depression was upon us.

"Dad, by then, was gradually edging back into the cigar business, but people had little money for luxuries. He would more often than not swap a box of cigars for a couple dozen eggs, a gallon of milk, corn on the cob, potatoes, etc. We ate potato soup several times a week. Times were tough then.

"By the Summer of 1933, I was 12 years old. The owner of our family's rented house left a rusted out 1926 Jordan 4-door auto in the barn at the rear of his city lot. I told Dad that I'd like to repair it for our family use, and he bought it from the landlord for $10. I borrowed a battery and tried to start it, but the engine was locked up and would not crank. So, I took the engine apart, ground the valves, removed the pistons, honed the cylinders, and put in new piston rings that were slightly larger than the old ones. My cousin Vernon worked for United Parts Company and got the parts at his employee discount. He patiently answered my many questions as I tore apart and rebuilt that sick engine. I sanded down the body by hand, and with a paintbrush, primed and painted it with Dupont olive-colored lacquer.

"The acid test finally arrived. I turned on the ignition, stomped on the starter button, and...BANG! BANG, CHUG, CHUG...*BANG!* Pitch black smoke poured out of the exhaust pipe. I was disappointed with tears pouring down my face...the bitter taste of defeat was mine. Dad saw my distress, put his arms around my shoulders and quietly said: 'Son, I have a friend who is a mechanic, and I bet he will come over and correct what is wrong for a box of cigars.'

"He did. The problem was that I didn't have the plug wires going to the proper holes in the distributor—a simple mistake. Dad's mechanic friend then showed me how to time the engine, starting with the reference mark on the flywheel, then placing the wires into the distributor cap as shown on the firing order that was stamped on the cylinder head. Success! The junked straight-eight Jordan ran smoothly, and Dad used that car for the next ten years. We even drove it to Cincinnati and back!

"That one experience was a life-changing moment for me; I learned that if I put my whole energy and purpose into a seemingly impossible task, in time the outwardly impossible might well be accomplished.

"At age 14, I started high school at Lane Tech in Chicago. It was a super high school with rows of fully-equipped machine tools of all types; an aviation shop to repair and study airplanes; print shops; chemistry and physics labs; mechanical drawing classrooms; electric shops; woodworking shops; photo labs;

Lane Tech, Chicago

auto repair shops...that school had it all. Lane Tech published a monthly magazine, *Tech Prep*, and a daily newspaper. I became the technical editor for the magazine for three years, and the principal editor for the school yearbook in my senior year.

Wes as editor surrounded by his staff

American Television Institute

"As the technical editor, one of my articles was 'How Television Works.' In researching material for the article, I visited the American Television Institute in downtown Chicago and was introduced to U. A. Sanabria, who ran the school. During the interview session, I asked Mr. Sanabria if he would like to buy the back-cover ad space for the *Tech Prep* issue that my article would appear in. He asked, 'How much?' I said $25 and told him that I just happened to have an ad space contract with me, which he warmly signed. Now, what I quoted wasn't a bargain-basement price, but I figured with my article, that space was worth twice what others likely would pay.

"Of course, and only a month after the magazine was published with the TV article, my faculty sponsor collared me and said the school had not been paid. So, I went back to American TV and told the receptionist that I wanted to see Mr. Sanabria. After about two hours, I told her to remind Mr. Sanabria that I was still waiting. She did, and after a few minutes he came out of his office and coldly told me he was still busy. At this point, I said, 'Tell Mr. Sanabria that I am prepared to wait until Hell freezes over to collect the $25 due.' I wanted my commission for that ad, since it was for $2.50—which at that time was big money, in 1938! And, yes, I soon left with the 25 bucks!"

American Television Institute advertisement

As difficult as the Depression years were, they did equip the youth of that time to steel themselves for tough times, appreciate the value of an education, and to seize every opportunity to succeed. This was also a period when interest in radio was growing at a fever's pitch. The ability to communicate over long distances without wires had captured the imagination of people young and old, and Wes Schum was clearly in that number. Although determined to get that old Jordan back on the road, he was also becoming interested in understanding the magic of radio and how all things electronic worked.

While the technical editor for his high school's *Tech Prep* magazine, Wes learned of a fire alarm system newly installed by the City of Chicago. Sensing a potential story, he went to city hall and asked to interview persons involved in the design of that new system. Soon he was pointed to the contractor, Mr. Berkey Cover, Sr.

The two formed a fast friendship, and Wes was invited to Cover's home for dinner and to meet his family. Next came an invitation to visit Cover's factory, the Cover Dual-Signal Company, where Mr. Cover had developed and manufactured a fire/police alarm system that used no vacuum tubes. Cover had invented and patented a high-powered DC-operated microphone, which was called the Electra-Voice microphone. Using a combination of asbestos and carbon granules, Electra-Voice could develop high audio levels without tube amplification.

Cover's Electra-Voice microphone was developed in the mid-1920s, long before the Electro-Voice Company, itself a maker of microphones and one that exists today, was formed by others. Keep Berkey Cover and the Cover Dual-Signal Company in mind, as each played an important role in keeping Wes out of World War II and very much in the thick of electronics design and manufacturing.

Being the technical editor of Lane Tech's magazine had perks other than the obvious. You see, Lane Tech was an all-boys school; Wes conceived the brilliant idea of writing a monthly column, *The Girl on the Campus*. Doing so presented an interesting dilemma, since there were no girls enrolled on campus of the all-boys school. But why should that be an obstacle for a guy like Wes Schum? Of course, the column became quite popular and was eagerly awaited by Lane Tech students!

In sourcing "material" for his articles, Wes would visit the city's premier high schools and seek out the most beautiful girls he could find. (Yes, he readily claimed there was no shortage of viable subjects.) With a photographer in tow, he'd snap interesting action-situation photos and would run the interviewee through a gamut of questions such as: What do you like best about Lane Tech boys? What school clubs are you involved with? Do you like to dance? Would you like to meet later for a milkshake?

With his natural good looks, resonant voice, ready smile, and razor-sharp wit, our man Wesley did quite well for himself!

Girl on campus with Wes

Getting back to 1938 under the shadow of growing hostilities in Europe, Wes aimed for one last article quest for his *Tech Prep* magazine: “How Steel is Made.” He and his photographer traveled to a steel mill on Chicago’s far south side but didn’t get far beyond the mill’s massive all-steel (of course) front gate.

The two were aggressively cross-examined by plant security. The guards were each as cold as ice and had faces that seemed etched in granite. Forget the camera. No pictures were allowed, period.

To their surprise and instead of being tossed out on their ears, the two were led by armed escort throughout a few superficial areas of the plant and then sent on their way. From start to finish, the session lasted less than one hour. A condition of their visit was any resultant draft article had to be submitted and reviewed by plant security prior to publication. While there was no indication of what would subsequently happen if that article review ‘request’ was somehow ignored, it was obvious from the manner and tone in which they were so instructed that the result would be a wholly unpleasant one.

Just for the record, the pair’s steel mill article never made it to the printer; the plant’s security review stopped it cold in its tracks. You see, the steel mill Wes picked wasn’t making tin cans. It was making steel plate to be used for battleships and aircraft carriers in what was to become World War II. Strict censorship of technical journals and news articles soon became the norm as the clouds of war gathered over the world, which is hard to envision in the landscape of today’s 24-hour non-stop news cycle and opinion-biased media.

Chapter 2: The Radio Bug Bites

The year was 1937, and Wes found himself with a new locker partner at Lane Tech. His name was Bob Goldberg, who would eventually become W9ZDK. Bob had been experimenting with radio at home and invited Wes to see his "radio station." Bob had fashioned his setup from a mashup of parts on a plywood board, perched on the family's former kitchen table. He attached a wire about four feet long from the radio's circuitry to the on-off pull cord for the kitchen light. A single-bulb light illuminated the room.

Bob next plugged another cord into the AC wall socket, and soon the two heard a ham operator calling "CQ five meters." Picking up what looked like a telephone microphone, he nervously called the other station. What was said and how Bob managed to be heard is lost to time. Of course, neither Wes nor Bob had FCC licenses, which could not have gone unnoticed by the CQer.

The two were ham radio bootleggers!

Putting the no-license issue aside for the moment, the stars, sunspots, and Sporadic-E must all have been in perfect alignment since our two heroes were soon talking Chicago to New York on five meters with a 4-ft. long wire antenna! Wes was duly impressed and began studying everything he could find about VHF radio. Only when the two began poring over the *ARRL Handbook*, reading it cover to cover, did they discover a ham radio license was necessary. Did not having a license in any way stop their at-home radio transmission experiments? Nope, not for a moment. They'd get around to getting a license in due time.

(Note to current readership: Today's FCC takes a very dim view of unlicensed radio operations, ham radio or otherwise, so don't try this at home. Study hard, get your license, and do it the right way!)

To satisfy his growing thirst for radio, Wes began scouring the neighborhood for old equipment and soon collected bushel baskets of old battery type and early AC model radio sets—all of which were dutifully reduced to component-part form. Those parts became the foundation of an intense trial by (many) error education in radio. Eventually, those lashed together experiments led to a homebrewed pair of type 56 triodes gradually configured into a push-pull oscillator. By carefully cross slotting the two tube bases, he could get the oscillator to run at 188MHz (as determined by Letcher wire measurement). Next, he built a regenerative receiver around another 56 triode, coupled an antenna, and heard… nothing. What Wes needed was an advanced, companion experimenter to spur him on.

Today, ham operators call people who point others along a true path *Elmers*. I've never liked the term Elmer; to me, it conjures up images of a hapless Elmer Fudd. What's wrong with the term *mentor*?

That mentoring companion came in 1938 and in the form of Oliver Lepanen, who built a similar oscillator and receiver using type 76 tubes. The two boys constructed antennas on their back porches and were able to communicate (by hit-and-miss Morse code) over the one mile that separated their homes. Next, they built modulators for voice-radio experiments.

(A modulator is an electronics-based way of imparting voice information onto a radio signal. As it happens, voice information can be added onto a radio signal by altering the signal's amplitude, frequency, or phase. The process the boys used was amplitude modulation. Now, back to the story.)

Wes constructed a Heising plate modulator using two vacuum tubes. Oliver adapted a four-tube public address amplifier to become his modulator. During their first on-air amplitude modulated test contact—QSO, in ham-language—each tried for more and more audio power. Oliver's signal grew louder and louder, at least until it abruptly died. Oliver had cranked his modulation level up so high that the glass exploded right off his oscillator tubes! Poor Oliver was QRT, or off the air, until he could scrounge up replacement oscillator tubes.

Oliver Lepanen in action

Plenty of other Wes and Oliver radio adventures were yet to be had. One fateful evening, Wes heard his pal calling him via his receiver's loudspeaker. Wanting to try a pair of earphones that he had found tossed in with another basket of radios to cannibalize, he plugged them into the receiver's audio jack, placed the earphones on his head, reached for the transmitter's microphone, and touched the toggle switch. *BANG!* Wes next found himself laid out on the floor, looking at the ceiling and seeing bright, sparkling stars.

Not realizing what had happened and being somewhat disoriented, Wes dusted himself off, got back into his chair, put the earphones (aka cans) back on, and reached for the same switch...and got blasted again. It appears that not much had changed since the fork in the outlet days!

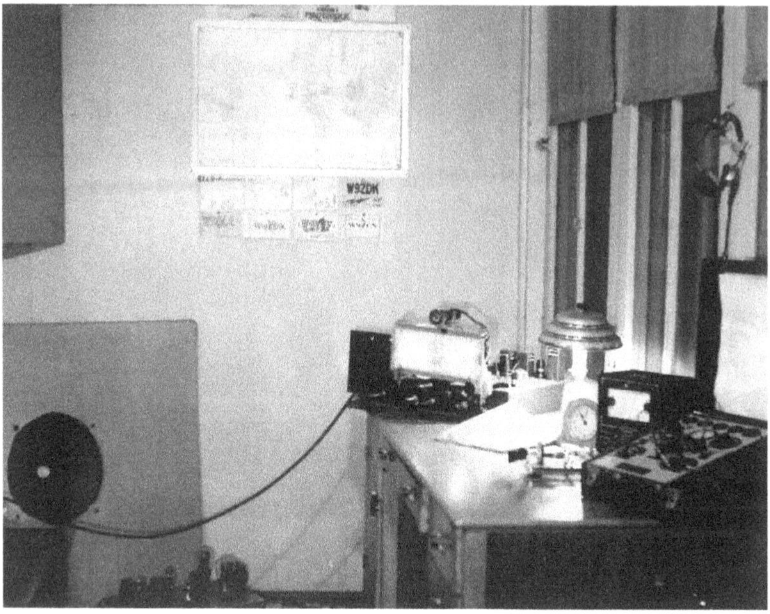

Early Radio Shack

Those old earphones were tossed out as trash *for a reason*. They were formed of painted metal but heavy usage had worn the paint off. What was left was shiny steel: highly *conductive* steel. The metal earphones, when connected to the receiver, had floated up to the tube's plate voltage (B+) level via the receiver; when touching the grounded toggle switch bar with his finger, Wes found himself being electrocuted by a couple hundred volts via the eardrums. Since the electrocution caper happened twice in rapid succession, perhaps this was irrefutable proof of the young man's hard-headed determination?

By early 1939, Wes had built a Meissner 14-tube receiver from a kit, was studying Morse code on 40 meters, and was steadily building up code speed. It was well past time to become a *legal* ham radio operator. In the fall of that year, Wes finally passed that all-important Class B license exam and became *W9DYV*. Wasting no time, he cleared the Class A upgrade test hurdle months later; soon after, Wes crossed paths with Roy Sherman, W9FHS, who was also an ardent radio experimenter and would become a life-long friend.

Together, Wes and Roy built rigs for 160 meters and soon developed a network of young Chicago-area ham friends. Their hangout was 1804kHz and grew to include W9VHW, W9USK, W9SCN and many others. The group even crafted their own "1804 network certificate!"

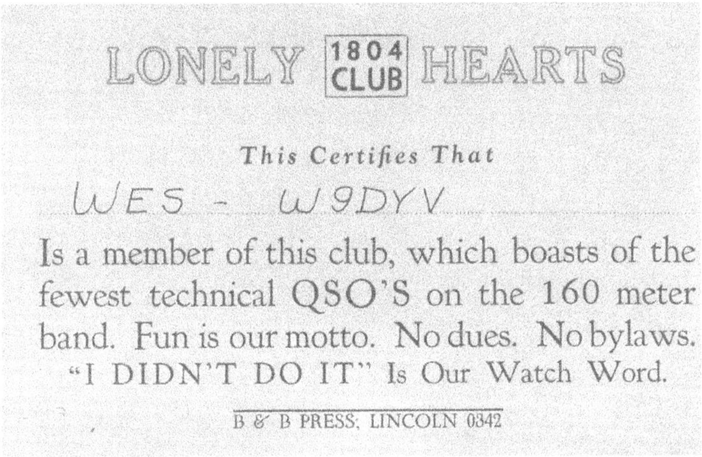

LONELY 1804 CLUB HEARTS

This Certifies That

WES - W9DYV

Is a member of this club, which boasts of the fewest technical QSO'S on the 160 meter band. Fun is our motto. No dues. No bylaws.

"I DIDN'T DO IT" Is Our Watch Word.

B & B PRESS; LINCOLN 0342

1804 network certificate

The 1804 game plan would involve chatting on air until 9 p.m., going QRT (aka "pulling the big switch," or shutting down operations) and next heading out to meet at a favorite ice cream parlor. Then, 25 cents would get you a full-quart milkshake loaded up with fantastic homemade ice cream.

If you can find one of those shakes today, plan on spending at least eight to ten bucks!

With his curiosity about ham radio growing by the day, Wes next ventured onto 75-meter phone to widen his area of signal reach. While Morse code (CW) was a licensing test requirement and essential for the Class A and B licenses, he never really enjoyed code and was totally interested in voice communications. So, he quickly found a weekend home on a 75-meter phone, where signal propagation for him and his limited antenna system was far better than on 160 meters. But 75 meters was a roiling, crowded mess on weekends, with all sorts of voice interference and beat notes (heterodynes) from one end of the band to the other.

Only guys having superior antennas, high powered transmitters, and rock-crushing signals made it through unscathed.

To Wes, this was just another challenge to overcome. *Something* about cutting through this heterodyne nonsense had to be found! Yet, those inventive thoughts ground to a halt as soon the World was at war and the amateur radio service was mothballed by the federal government.

Chapter 3: A Radio Profession Is Born

Wes graduated from Lane Tech High School in late 1939, and by then wanted desperately to design and build radios. After school, he could always find time to drift by the E.H. Scott Company on Ravenswood Avenue. E.H. Scott was a premier builder of the highest quality radio sets, all custom made to order. Only the very well-heeled owned Scotts.

The Scott factory had a row of windows along the ground floor that looked into the radio assembly area. There, Wes could be found on tiptoes, sneaking peeks and watching radios being built, his imagination running at high speed.

Eventually his spying caught the watchful eye of the shop steward, and soon after came a tap on the shoulder. Wes was busted! After hearing how interested this young man was in radio and manufacturing, he was ushered into the building and got to see those masterful Scott radios being made up close and personal. In time, he met several design engineers, model makers, assembly managers, and many others. In short, he received an excellent behind-the-scenes view of radio design, manufacturing, and testing that only served to cement his desire to enter this field of work professionally.

Scott had no openings at the time, in the Depression years, but the shop steward suggested Radio Products Corporation, which was then the manufacturing arm of Admiral Corp. There Wes met Lovell Crawford, W9BYZ, who was the chief inspector at Radio Products. With his ham radio background, Wes was soon loaded up with part-time work on the assembly line. Seeing how productive this new hire had become, Lovell then brokered a meeting for Wes with the firm's CEO, Ken Turner, and a new important friendship was born. Ken was building a radio-controlled boat on his off-time and recruited young Schum to help him design and build its electronics. The 'sea trial' was held on the Rock River, north of Chicago.

It must have been fun, watching people stare at the boat while it conducted all sorts of maneuvers—particularly when the boat glided stealthily to the dock, with no one on-board at the helm!

E.H. Scott Company

During this period, Wes was a true bundle of electronic energy. He designed and built Hi-Fi AM radio/audio systems for his parents' friends (and barroom operators) from components purchased from electronic parts emporiums in downtown Chicago. His creations included hand-drawn dial scales, huge 15-inch dynamic loudspeakers, and separate bass and treble controls. These sets sounded great, selling for $300 a unit from his front porch; a cottage manufacturing business of sorts grew from word of mouth.

Expanding this entertainment business enterprise a step further, Wes became an independent radio repairman for the city's Good Housekeeping Furniture stores. Good Housekeeping had employed 12 field service men, and Wes became number 13. Soon, Wes became Good Housekeeping's go-to man, repairing the dog radios that field service men could not fix by changing tubes at the customer's home.

One day, an urgent call came in to field repair a customer's pricey Scott Philharmonic radio. The set worked fine on the broadcast band, but its shortwave performance was poor.

Now, this customer was no regular Joe; he was the Italian consul, and required his radio to hear shortwave stations in Italy (keep in mind the War in Europe was then underway, with the US sitting on the sidelines). Wes sized things up and installed a rooftop antenna, matching the antenna's impedance to the radio's input. When finished, the two then sat back and enjoyed the wonderful music booming in from Rome. The man was hugely impressed and insisted Wes share a glass of vino to mark the occasion, as well as take home a $20 tip as a token of appreciation. Then, $20 was nearly a week's wages for many.

Consulate's Scott Philharmonic radio

By 1940, the US was heavily into its Lend-Lease program with England, and Congress was working at breakneck speed to convert America's manufacturing might from a peacetime to a wartime footing. Contracts for all sorts of war time items began to flow, and much of that increased production need involved electronics devices and systems.

One Chicago outfit pitching hard to gain a share of that work was the Cover Dual-Signal Corporation. But Cover Dual-Signal had a problem: The shop's production manager had died, and a replacement was needed immediately. Mr. Cover thought long and hard, then remembered that young man from Lane Tech. Maybe that Schum guy would be interested? He seemed to be an electronics wiz.

He was a wiz, had progressed a long way since his first introduction to Berkey Cover, and was very much interested.

With notice given to Good Housekeeping, Wes soon joined Cover Dual-Signal Systems. There, he found a shop that was structured to build one product: police and fire alarm boxes. These were located at street corners and were connected by wires to a central city dispatcher. However, the military wasn't interested in wire-connected alarm boxes. What the military wanted was radio-linked alarm boxes for use on military bases and ammunition storage sites; they were needed fast, and in large quantities.

This one order required a whole new approach, and Wes had a ready answer. He had been experimenting with VHF radio gear for some years by that time and had built several transmitters using the new "instant on" tubes that had recently come to market. Armed with an idea of how to solve the problem, experienced radio hands were needed.

To beef up Cover's engineering capability overnight, Wes tapped the most obvious (to him) talent source: ham radio. All his ham friends were experimenters, and some had built incredibly complex radios that were seriously pushing the envelope. In days, several were working for Cover's operation; most importantly, Schum's best friend and excellent radio engineer, Roy Sherman, had agreed to join them too.

Wes Schum and Roy Sherman

As work progressed on proof-of-concept models, attention was next drawn to the manufacturing and test capability of the shop. Initially, those capabilities were surprisingly thin; Wes was handed a clean, empty slate that needed filling fast.

Mr. Cover was all in and bankrolled the company's rapid expansion through bank loans and personal investment. Soon, Wes was attending auctions of older fabrication equipment to see if such equipment could be bought for a song and "rehabilitated" for Cover's production needs. Never buy new if those dollars could be best applied to product research was his motto, with Berkey Cover's full support. Every dollar spent had to do the work of two, if not more.

In time, used but usable punch presses, finger brakes, shears, lathes, milling machines, vibration chambers, and other such apparatuses started rolling in, each having a planned function in Wes' mind. Transformer winding machines, vacuum impregnation tanks, and high/low temperature test chambers were next. Wes had seen these types of machines in constant action at both E.H. Scott and Radio Products Corporation. He knew what they did, how they should be maintained, and where they were most efficiently used. If there was any doubt, a swift eight city-block walk to friends at Scott Radio would set him straight. You see, Scott was located at 4450 North Ravenswood, while Cover Dual-Signal's building was situated at 5215-25 North Ravenswood. How convenient!

The new alarm system's metal fabrication at Cover Dual was coming together nicely, in large part because of a dynamite modelmaker named Nick Fishik. Nick and metal fabrication seemed intertwined. But what about test equipment? Here, the surplus equipment route was no good. Wes knew Cover needed the best and most advanced test equipment available to produce highest quality, most reliable wartime products.

For signal sources, component standards, and quality control instrumentation, the choices were the General Radio Company and the newly formed Measurements Corporation. Equipment Wes sourced from General Radio catapulted Cover Dual-Signal into the highest tier for frequency accuracy, in step with the best metrology labs of the time. The inherent accuracy of those General Radio tools allowed Cover to hold outside component suppliers to the strictest, highest quality standards.

Peacetime quality was no quality, as far as the US military was concerned. Wartime equipment suppliers understood the lives of service personnel relied on every piece of hardware or component manufactured. Their products were not needed for backyard BBQs or a night on the town. Their purpose was singular: an all-out fight for democracy's survival. Reliability and performance during the worst of operational conditions was essential.

With Wes calling the engineering shots, all was proceeding to Berkey Cover's satisfaction. Cover Dual continued to make its legacy product unimpeded while Wes structured the firm to build wartime products to far higher performance standards.

Then it happened, and the world held its breath: Japan attacked the United States naval fleet parked at Pearl Harbor, Hawaii on December 7th, 1941—a date young Wes would remember for the rest of his life. You see, Wesley R. Schum had been born at home on that same day, twenty years earlier.

Wes Schum and newly installed GR gear

Cover Dual machine shop

Roy Sherman wiring transmitter modules

Chapter 4: Schum on the Home Front

That Sunday morning of December 7th, 1941 changed life in the United States in an instant. People were incensed that Japan attacked, killing or wounding thousands of young servicemen. Soon, President Roosevelt was asking Congress to declare war on Japan, but even before that could happen—in the dark, uncertain hours after the attack—many rushed to Army and Navy recruitment offices to volunteer for action. America's fight was to be one of no-holds-barred survival.

Berkey Cover, Sr. was ready for his company to join the fight, but first he had to lock down his head man, Wes Schum. Cover sprang into action and filed for military exemptions to keep Schum out of the fight and at his desk. Without him, Cover Dual would have been unable to complete the war contracts it had already accepted, and those involved important security systems for Army/Navy bases. Word came down quickly that Schum was out of the war, at least for the foreseeable future. It was time to get rolling.

The first products sourced by the US military were fire and police alarm systems for its base facilities. Those were to utilize FM radio as the linkage medium. A second life-saving project involved electronic systems for an improved paravane torpedo defense system to protect supply transports and US naval vessels. Of course, the needed military base alarm equipment didn't fully exist in Cover Dual's catalog, but

Wes was ahead of the curve. He and his team had by then developed a new radio unit to meet the need. Cover Dual's radio assembly was quickly approved for production by the Office of Production Management. Quantity contracts were established with firm delivery dates and pricing, and the heat was on Cover Dual to deliver at double-time speed.

Cover's standard wireline alarm equipment enclosure and hardware was up to the task. All that was needed was a rugged radio package that could operate in weather extremes (heat or cold, in rain, ice, and snow) and was energy efficient, since the equipment must operate from a 6V or 12V DC battery source. That radio package became Wes Schum's first war contribution.

The radio was fashioned as a two-chassis design, allowing physical and electrical separation between transmitter and receiver circuitry. Doing so eliminated any tendency for self-interference and simplified unit assembly. The radios were crystal controlled and operated over the range of 30MHz to 40MHz. All tubes were low voltage (1.5V filament), instant-on types to eliminate unnecessary battery current drain. In normal operation, with the alarm unit's door closed, both transmitting and receiving units were disabled. Once the door was opened, filament voltage was applied to the receiver, thereby prepping it for instant operation. B+ voltage (90 volts or abbreviated as 90V) for the receiver's vacuum tubes was derived from the alarm unit's 6V or 12V battery pack via a vibrator-type voltage converter.

Cover Dual Receiver by Wes

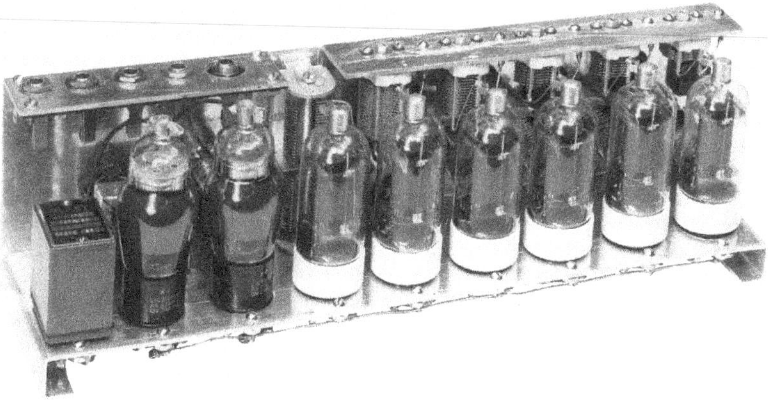

Cover Dual Transmitter by Wes

The transmitter likewise contained instant-on tubes but had two B+ power supplies. The unit's oscillator and doubler stages were powered like the receiver but used a separate 90V vibrator system. The unit's final amplifier and driver stages, since they required higher voltages and currents, were powered by a dynamotor. Whenever the transmitter's push-to-talk button was initially depressed, that action would light the transmitter's tube filaments and start the vibrator supply. A separate 450V dynamotor would then start and provide appropriate driver/ power amplifier plate voltage. When unkeyed, the dynamotor would be immediately turned off, but the filament and vibrator supplies (both receiver and transmitter) remained active for a predetermined period. This was done to further improve transmitter key-up response time.

Since alarm systems of this type are used intermittently, the battery life intervals between replacement or recharging were materially extended using Schum's power scheme.

The transmitter's power output was rated at 15 watts. The unit's companion receiver had a guaranteed sensitivity of 1uV and would achieve FM quieting at 1.5uV. In addition, both the transmitter and receiver units contained audio filters to limit the system's voiced audio to 3kHz, thereby increasing and enhancing intelligibility. All transmitter stages included metering jacks for simplified testing and alignment, and once fabricated, completed assemblies were appropriately impregnated with moisture and fungus protective coatings.

Each alarm box was designed for easy operation, with easy-to-understand instructions engraved into the unit's cover. The top of each alarm unit's cast aluminum enclosure included a red alarm alert light and an integral base-loaded antenna. By so doing, field installation of a unit could be completed in an hour's time.

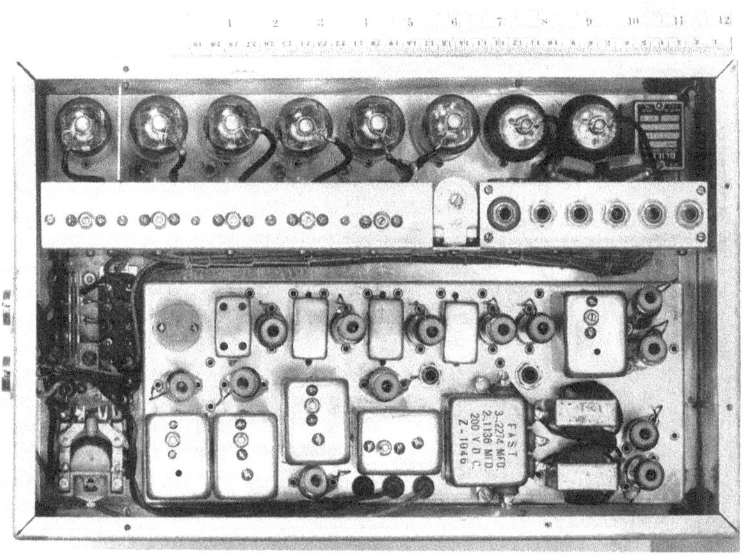

Complete Cover Dual Receiver/Transmitter

A corresponding alarm monitoring console configuration allowed security personnel to easily monitor each remote alarm unit as activated and to communicate back via radio as needed. Considering the period of this alarm system's design and the performance of readily available electronic components in late 1939, the guaranteed performance of this equipment was superb.

Moving on, the torpedo paravane project was one designed to protect US shipping and personnel. A life-saving product, it was placed on an emergency-development fast track. The German Wolfpack was decimating merchant mariner shipping prior to the US official entry into the war. Over the period of 1939 through 1943, some 5,758 ships were lost due to torpedo sinkage. The toll on personnel and lost vital equipment was staggering.

Originally developed during WWI, paravanes were intended to neutralize mines in harbors. Their role had expanded in WWII; they were needed not only to detonate mines or sink submarines, but also to kill deployed torpedoes before they struck supply ships.

In theory, it went this way: Sets of paravanes would be towed behind surface ships, usually by mine tenders. Staggered along the tow lines were remotely detonated explosive charges. If an explosive-equipped paravane encountered an object, such as a mine or submarine, it could be remotely exploded and neutralize the threat. But how to *automatically* neutralize a fast-moving torpedo?

Paravane release

That's where Cover Dual's project award came into play.

The concept was to install hydrophones (underwater microphones) on the tow ship and secondary sets of hydrophones on the paravane tow lines. The US Navy and Signal Corps had studied the electrically-operated propeller sounds from German torpedoes and had isolated the range of frequencies torpedoes made while speeding through water. What if a device could be made that monitored the sounds picked up from the hydrophones and automatically triggered a dynamite charge, should a torpedo closely approach the tow vessel or lines? Making that important sound detection apparatus was Cover Dual's assignment.

In concept, what was needed was a frequency selective amplifier, tuned to the German torpedo's screw pitch (measured as 54kHz). Once the detected 54kHz sound level reached a high preset threshold, which would occur should a speeding torpedo approach one or more hydrophones, the frequency selective amplifier(s) would send a detonate signal to the nearest trailing dynamite charge.

Cover Dual was well underway with this project when Wes joined the team, but it had run into a snag: the frequency selective amplifier would intermittently function. It wouldn't outright fail, but it would occasionally fail to activate. Even an occasional failure of that type would clearly be catastrophic. A solution had to be found—and fast.

Already the company's engineers had been pouring on the coals to get to a solution, but none was to be had. The intermittent problem would come and go like a ghost, never long enough that it could be pinned down. And worse, it seemed to affect different stages in the amplifier/detector scheme at different intervals.

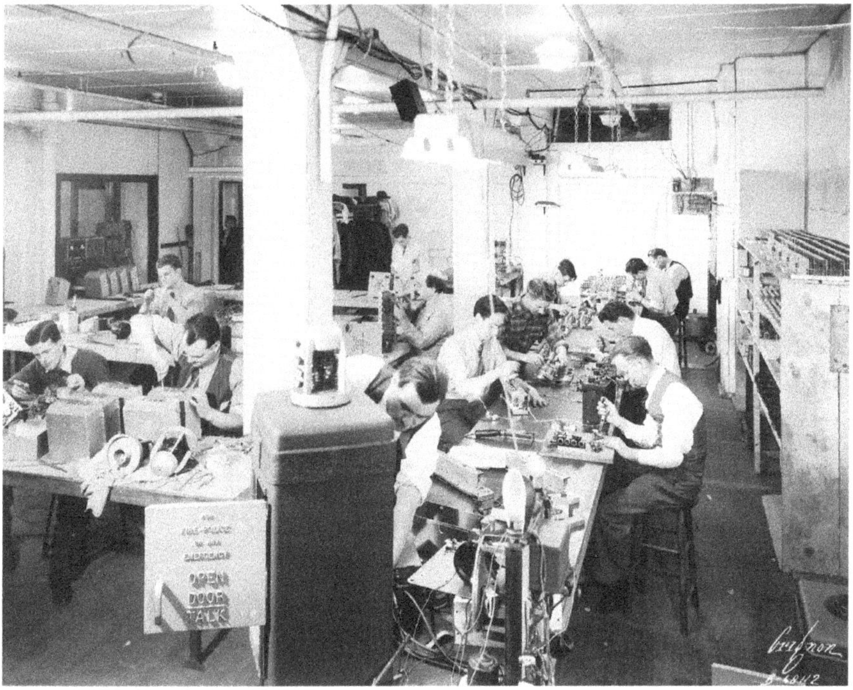

Cover Dual factory

It was maddening. Production was falling way behind; money was being lost.

Always on everyone's mind was the knowledge that ships, precious cargoes, and crews were being lost daily. The screws were being tightened on Cover Dual. Wes and his crews were hard at work, but their efforts seemingly made little difference. It was a period of total frustration and anxiety. Everyone was pulling long hours through weekends to get a repeatable, stable solution. It just wasn't happening. Worse still, Mr. Cover, "The Boss," was getting increasingly frustrated and more short-tempered by the minute.

Berkey Cover was a sight of a man. Tall, rather rotund, and well-dressed complete with pocket watch—and usually an unlit cigar stub clamped in his mouth. He had a booming voice and was never afraid to use it. His management style was intimidation. As his anger progressed, that cigar stub would wander from one side of his mouth to the other, somehow remaining in one piece. In short, he was feared rather than respected. Cover rarely had a kind word for the workers; in fact, his usual mode was to dress down his employees. Most made a point to become somewhat invisible whenever he ventured onto the shop floor.

Berkey Cover with engineers

Cover Dual-Signal Lab

It was destined to happen, and it did, one eventful Monday morning.

The entire engineering team and Wes had spent a long, worrisome weekend working full throttle, with precious little sleep and just running on fumes. On Monday morning, Cover barged in, and sensing no solution was at hand, went on an absolute shout fest of a tirade. He got into every visible man's face and belittled them, individually and personally. His favorite derogatory term was *Peckerwood*, and he would yell this to each errant employee at ear-splitting volume.

Wes had had enough. As "The Boss" stormed back into his plush office, Wes was flying low right behind him, stepping through the door just as the big man sat down in his high-backed leather chair, slamming the door hard behind him. It was a wonder the door's signature glass panel didn't shatter into a million pieces. Wes Schum rarely had an uncontrolled fit of temper, but today was the day. His team had been working their hearts out, and he didn't appreciate Cover's demeanor one damned bit.

Like a prizefighter eager for blood, Wes methodically went after Cover with no holds barred. First, he charged in hard and told Cover his attitude and hot-headed noise made him look like the big jackass that he was. Next, he declared that his team were actual human beings with feelings and emotions, and Cover's outbursts were killing their ability to concentrate and perform. Then, for the *fait accompli*: Wes shot up even closer and while standing within two inches of Cover's shocked eyes, shouted for him to *NEVER* call him or anyone else Peckerwood, ever again—and to never talk to him with that damned smelly cigar in his mouth, either.

Berkey Cover was so taken aback by the force and savagery of Wes' counterattack that he swallowed the stubby cigar end that had previously been clamped in his teeth.

Wes, some years later, recalled it was like a light switch was thrown. Cover's disposition abruptly changed, at least after he had a minute to recover from the shock. Berkey Cover had never once been dressed down in that manner, and it either embarrassed him or gave him pause to think. No matter; what he did next was to apologize to Wes sincerely and contritely. Then he walked out onto the shop floor and apologized to each of the engineers, individually, for his actions.

At the end of this incident, Wes said the shop was dead quiet. Maybe everyone was in shock. Soon, the various teams went back to work, but with a bit more spring in their steps. Berkey Cover had shown a bit of humility they had never seen previously in the man, and in Wes, they had found a young engineering manager who had brains, grit, and more importantly, had their backs and valued personal sacrifice.

Wes working at Berkey's desk

Later that week, the team's engineers figured out the problem. It involved intermittent short-circuits within molded mica capacitors. Mica capacitors had been selected due to their normally high reliability and installed as part of the product's frequency-selective amplifiers tuned to the torpedo screw frequencies. While the mica capacitors were checked by the parts supplier as well as inspected and tested again for value by Cover, using in-house test equipment, the parts were not being tested for capacity while impressed with a DC bias voltage.

One team member, exhausted and clutching at straws, did a DC bias test on a random sample of micas and noticed an occasional glitch. The problem was one caused by the outside supplier's manufacturing process, and outside of Cover's immediate control.

Once the parts were replaced by those from a different manufacturer, the problem was solved. Cover Dual quickly began to ship complete, tested, and *reliable* amplifier packages to a very eager customer. Eventually, word filtered back to Cover that tests on the torpedo-killing paravanes had met all expectations. Some killed German torpedoes had been recovered by the Navy, and as Wes later recalled, a set of Navy-supplied pictures showed a pile of killed torpedoes, each mashed as flat as a pancake!

It is impossible to tell how many lives or tons of materials were saved by those torpedo-tuned paravanes, but in 1942, 1,859 ships were lost; yet in 1943, that number had dropped to 814, once the equipment was installed and had made it to sea.

Other interesting projects came down the road. Wes soon found himself on a train to Boston, heading for the Radiation Lab at the Massachusetts Institute of Technology (MIT). Cover Dual had secured a contract with the US Army Air Corps involving the supply of devices for a new technology called radio detection and ranging, or RADAR, then being studied by researchers at MIT. The train rides would continue, with each return from MIT bringing a cake tin of breadboarded circuitry. Cover Dual's job was to repackage those cake tin circuits into reproducible items. A particularly interesting one carried home resulted in a microwave wave meter device that eventually was supplied by Cover Dual to the Signal Corps.

This device, the TS-69, was a frequency meter with a coverage range of 340MHz to 914MHz. The TS-69 was designed in 1941 and used to test and calibrate new and then highly secret RADAR transmitters. It consisted of a precision variably tuned cavity filter, mechanical turns counter, microammeter/RF detector, and tuning chart.

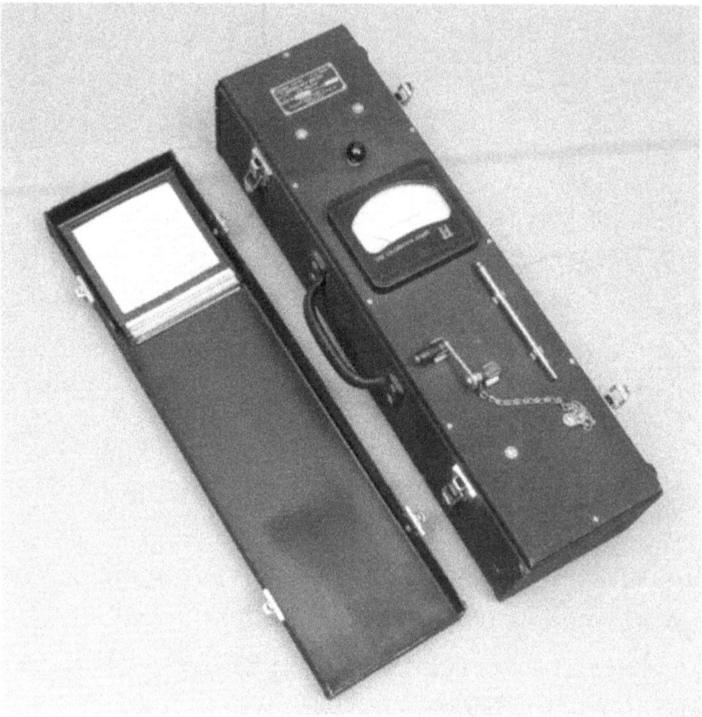

TS-69 frequency meter

When operated, an unknown microwave signal would be applied to the cavity's RF input and a tuning crank handle turned until a level was spotted on the included RF detector's meter. This setting was then carefully peaked up on the meter and the turns counter's reading then read. By comparing the number of indicated counter turns against the nine-page integral calibration book included with each TS-69, one could then determine the unknown signal's true frequency.

The turns counter/calibration book was integral to each manufactured frequency meter package. Without its companion calibration book, a TS-69 became a precision piece of scrap metal. Several thousand of these devices were constructed throughout the war. The last version of the TS-69, the TS-69A, was supplied the Signal Corps in late 1944.

Another important project was secured by Cover that eventually brought Schum to Washington, DC. There he was to meet with a team of engineers with the Civil Aeronautics Administration to receive orders on a new undertaking. Cover Dual had been selected to construct the CAA's new Model TUL runway localizer transmitter, which was to become part of what was termed *Signal Set 51*: an instrument landing system for airplanes. Signal Set 51's purpose was to transmit navigation signals to incoming aircraft during periods of poor visibility. This device was to be installed throughout the US, and presumably, allied airport facilities worldwide.

Functionally, TUL transmitters were destined to be installed within concrete-enclosed, below-ground vaults located at both ends of a given aircraft runway. These concrete vaults were not environmentally hardened, and therefore essentially exposed to the elements: heat, cold, snow, ice, and rain. In short, a vault was an environment highly adverse to electronic equipment, particularly so for transmitters that operated at extremely high impressed voltages. The TUL transmitter was nevertheless required to survive that sort of environment and operate trouble-free for five years.

The TUL design and Signal Set 51 had an incredibly tall group of performance hurdles to clear. It was an all-new concept then. Wes, by then used to that sort of hardball assignment, assembled a team of thirty radio and fabrication specialists to construct TUL transmitters while meeting the CAA's strict performance specifications.

Unfortunately, just because a customer insists on a level of performance doesn't mean it can be met in reality.

It soon became obvious that the CAA's specified varnish-impregnated plate and screen voltage transformers would fail due to insulation breakdown, accelerated by the equipment vault's damp environmental conditions. Sensing the CAA design was destined to fail and would drag Cover Dual along with it, the company sent a letter to the CAA citing the many design deficiencies found and Wes' proposed design criteria for replacement transformers.

The CAA was not impressed and demanded a meeting with the upstart, Schum. So off he went, armed with a new transformer design and a humidity performance run completed on a CAA "spec-complaint" transformer, as was required by the contracted design.

Upon arrival, Wes was ushered into a meeting room filled with twenty engineers from throughout the nation. They were not pleased; this young man was calling their baby ugly, and worse. Who did this kid think he was dealing with?

First, Wes thanked everyone for the opportunity to meet, even though all knew that his meeting was not by invitation but a demand performance. That angry gathering was intent on stringing our young hero up by his thumbs.

No matter. Wes Schum was prepared for battle.

Wes spent the first 30 minutes describing Cover Dual's guaranteed performance concerns, one by one. The crew of twenty engineers never so much as blinked an eye. Those guys were as cold as icecaps on the North Pole. But then Wes unveiled a test sample of a CAA-compliant transformer that had been subjected to 70% humidity and high temperatures for a 30-day period. It was a total, rusted wreck. He had it mounted on a wooden board and fused.

Ready for the power-up acid test, folks?

Once plugged in and before the fuse had time to blow, which to all seemed an eternity, the room filled with pungent black smoke and alarmingly large sparks ensued. Mercifully, the fuse finally cleared, and everyone's eyeballs were opened wide, as big as cue balls. The icecap had melted!

After the yelling, noise, and smoke settled down, Wes then produced two alternative samples of hermetically sealed, pitch-filled transformers he had custom made. These were enclosed in drawn stainless steel containers and had air-tight ceramic bushings for all input and output connections. Each had stainless steel threaded connectors to eliminate corrosion. The first of two units produced had undergone the same humidity treatment as the burned-out CAA unit. The remaining unit was tested at 95% humidity.

Each of the Schum-designed alternative samples had emerged pristine from the humidity tests. Both operated at the CAA's specified excitation current and temperature rise and had met their dynamic voltage regulation target. Not only was the CAA sold on his improvement ideas, but all twenty engineers took a pause and gave Wes Schum a standing ovation. Heading for home, Wes had the important CAA project change order tucked in his briefcase and a smile painted on his face.

Cover Dual produced over 200 TUL transmitters that included Schum's demonstrated changes. Not only did they meet the CAA's five-year target, the TUL remained in service for *thirty-five* years, the last of which being retired when the power amplifier tubes it used were no longer available. Wes coached his team to never over-stress components and to build a conservative safety margin into all designs. It was a philosophy well embraced throughout his career, and one that likely saved servicemen's lives.

Cover Dual was awarded an important, revenue-generating project that kept its workforce churning at high revolutions. Throughout WWII, the firm reconditioned radiosondes, which are electronic weather devices carried into the stratosphere by balloons. At the upper altitudes, the balloons would eventually burst, and the radiosonde would descend via parachute back to Earth. On their way down, these units would accumulate data and send signals back to the ground stations that would then chart real-time weather statistics. This information was particularly important during bombing runs, where weather aspects such as wind speed, air density, temperature, and humidity could affect the accuracy of bomb delivery. Over the war's course, and by working dual shifts, over 50,000 radiosondes were reconditioned and returned to service by Cover Dual's ever-growing staff.

One of Wes' last but most advanced projects while at Cover Dual involved a joint effort with Northwestern University's research section, headed by Professor Robert Beam. Northwestern and the Department of Navy were working to develop a means for ship-to-ship communications over a beam of invisible light energy. If successful, that technology would permit highly secure ship-to-ship communications during battle of a form impervious to traditional radio eavesdropping.

Cover Dual's role was geared toward optimizing and packaging the system's electronics. The system's infrared light sources and receivers were installed on repurposed, stabilized gun mounts. Those mounts also included high-powered binoculars to facilitate initial source-to-receiver aiming. The light beam was amplitude modulated using a pair of 807s, a transmitting power tube any ham operator of the 1940s through the '60s would readily recognize.

On-water field tests of the various prototype systems were conducted on Lake Michigan, and the results deemed encouraging. These first prototypes could communicate over distances of 8 miles using modulated voice and up to 12 miles with modulated CW (Morse code), all on a beam of invisible light. The urgency of the Navy's need forced prototypes made by Cover Dual-Signal and independently by Belmont Radio into expedited production. Several hundred test and evaluation units were ultimately delivered by Cover Dual.

Continued testing and optimization of the infrared system was conducted in conjunction with Northwestern University, always in the often-rough waters of Lake Michigan. More work was needed to conclude the design process into a final, finished product, but then the war was showing promising signs of winding down in the Pacific. The development project, likewise, was soon abandoned. What those tests proved to Wes, though, was he was a certified landlubber, through and through. Every shipboard test he witnessed brought with it the agony of sea-sickness.

In fact, as 1944 ended, the need for huge quantities of electronic equipment and heavy product research for the war effort done by smaller plants like Cover Dual was receding fast. New equipment contracts were thinning out, and Wes figured Cover Dual might not survive without them. In the early years of the war, the business had grown like it was on steroids. Berkey Cover had the illusion that the gravy train would never end—but of course it did. The federal government could not sustain the levels of wartime deficit spending without an eventual day of reckoning.

So, once the infrared project ended with the Navy, Wes' involvement with Cover Dual soon did as well. Perhaps those on-sea adventures in Lake Michigan prepared Wes to recognize when to abandon ship. He was quickly scooped up by the Electronics Communications Equipment Company, or ECEC, and made their chief engineer.

ECEC was also a Chicago equipment manufacturer, but unlike Cover Dual-Signal, the company was involved in the more fiscally stable, non-military railroad communications market. ECEC's product was wireline voice communication and rail management switchgear. Rail management involved not only systems for freight hauling, but also those for passenger trains and systems geared to municipal subways. Wes brought his best men from Cover Dual along, too. Guys like Roy Sherman and Nick Fishik, premier machinist and model maker extraordinaire, followed their leader.

But the stop at ECEC didn't last long for Wes. Once the war in Japan ended, his wartime deferment ended with it. Instantly, Wes Schum was fair game to be drafted! Sadly, Cover Dual was by then circling the drain. Its outstanding military contracts were quickly pulled by the government and Berkey Cover, Sr. found himself stuck holding the bag with nearly 150 employees, but no peacetime product, no work, and huge overhead costs.

Then, the worst happened: Berkey Cover died suddenly on December 16th, 1946. By July 1948, the company's bones had been picked clean in bankruptcy and the business was gone for good—not an uncommon tale for many once thriving businesses in the wake of World War II. The stress of uncertain times, the lack of post-war product markets, and fortunes lost seemingly overnight were insurmountable hurdles for many business owners. The stress of war and harsh, unrelenting production urgency sadly proved too much to bear for men like Berkey Cover.

UNITED STATES DISTRICT COURT
NORTHERN DISTRICT OF ILLINOIS
EASTERN DIVISION

REFEREES
WALLACE STREETER
NATHAN WILLIAM MACCHESNEY
AUSTIN HALL

TELEPHONE
HARRISON 4700

OFFICE OF
REFEREES IN BANKRUPTCY
UNITED STATES COURTHOUSE
225 S. CLARK STREET
CHICAGO 4, ILLINOIS

AUCTION

BY ORDER OF THE U. S. DISTRICT COURT FOR THE NORTHERN DISTRICT OF ILLINOIS, EASTERN DIVISION
We Will On

THURSDAY, JULY 8, 1948

AT 11:00 A.M. AT

5215-25 North Ravenswood Avenue

AND CONTINUING AT

5006 North Clark Street
Chicago, Illinois

SELL AT PUBLIC AUCTION
THE ASSETS OF

Cover Dual Signal Systems, Inc., A Corporation

Case No. 48 B 42 In Proceedings Under Chapter XI
MANUFACTURERS OF ELECTRONIC EQUIPMENT

CONSISTING OF
REAL ESTATE and PERSONAL PROPERTY
APPRAISAL VALUE APPROXIMATELY $300,000.00

EXHIBITION: ONE WEEK PRIOR TO SALE

HON. WALLACE STREETER
Referee in Bankruptcy

TELLER, LEVIT & SILVERTRUST
Attorneys for Debtor Corporation

For Further Information Phone, Wire or Write to

MICHAEL TAUBER & COMPANY *Auctioneers*

411 South Market Street Telephone Webster 4500 Chicago, Illinois

Cover Dual auction

Chapter 5: Drafted *After* the War!

The United States went nuts on August 14th, 1945 when victory over Japan had been accomplished. The soldiers were soon to be heading home. For Wes Schum, his personal war on the home front was over; his time to serve in the US Army had come.

He was being drafted!

The news came in the form of a letter: "Good news: Your neighbors have selected you to join the US Army! Report to Fort Sheridan on November 27th, 1945." That notice hit Wes like a ton of bricks. He knew he was likely to be inducted, but so soon after the war ended?

Another surprise awaited Wes Schum, but this one was far more welcome. The die was cast in 1945 for an eventual meeting that would change Schum's life forever. Wes had enrolled at the beginning of the year in an evening college mathematics class at the Carl Schurz Junior College on Milwaukee Avenue. His goal after high school was to work (eventually) toward a full electrical engineering degree, but the war and his work at Cover Dual-Signal had interrupted those plans. At the end of the 2nd semester of Math 102, the teacher asked for two students to rise from their seat. One was Marguerite (Marge) Aldridge, and the other... Who else? Wes Schum, of course. "Class," the teacher continued, "there were only two As this semester, and I want you folks to know them and observe."

Wes *observed*, all right. He was on high alert.

The two looked at each other and sparks flew! "Boy," Wes said to himself, "I want to know this young lady. She's beautiful, intelligent, and I have just *got* to get to know her!" As the class later concluded and the crowd began to break up, Wes made his well-calculated move: He asked Marge to join him for a milkshake. He had in mind the Buffalo Ice Cream Parlor, which was a favorite hangout for young people of that era. It was within walking distance, near Irving Park and Pulaski Street. As he held his breath, she smiled and said "OK!"

That was the beginning of a life-long relationship. The two studied trigonometry in preparation for the next fall semester over the summer break and were together every single day. In due course, V-J Day occurred in mid-August, and the war was ending for most. For the unknowing Wes Schum, his war just about to start. In late October, the two had started talking about a future together, but no firm date had been nailed down. *We've got time, right?* both of them likely thought.

The notice from Uncle Sam arrived in November 1945, and with it a non-threatening invitation to come in on November 27th for a 9 a.m. pre-induction physical. Wes figured the Army wasn't moving all that fast to add people to its ranks while simultaneously thinning them out. Surely, he'd go in for the physical and would then be given a future date to go into the service.

No, that wasn't it...not by a long shot.

Upon concluding (and passing) his physical, he was told a train would be leaving Chicago for Fort Sheridan at 3 p.m. that day, and he needed to be on it!

Somehow, Wes recovered from the shock and told the recruitment sergeant, "Whoa! I have a car parked down in a paid parking lot. I've got to take it back home, go to the office and explain why I'm suddenly unavailable, clear out my desk...all kinds of stuff!" The sergeant relented and said, "OK. Be back at the train station at 3 p.m. *tomorrow* to shove off!"

Oh, man. Wes desperately wanted to marry Marge, and it had to happen immediately. What to do? He had to move fast! First, Wes took care of the car and office loose ends. Next, he raced over to the university, explaining that he had been drafted and had to immediately drop out. His final stop was Marge's house, to figure things out. That was his first moment to catch a breath, much less form a coherent thought, but it was only just the beginning. All of Wes Schum's planning, organization, and must-win skills would be put to the ultimate test.

While holding hands that night, Wes looked into Marge's big brown eyes and quietly asked, "Will you please marry me tomorrow?" In semi-disbelief, Marge choked out, "Of course I will, Wes. But, how can we? You have to be on that train at three p.m. tomorrow?! We must have blood tests taken and get them approved by the Chicago Board of Health. And then we need to get a marriage license out of City Hall, somehow. How can we do all of that?!"

Wes sized it up and said, "Don't worry. We'll get it done, starting right now!" They jumped in his car and started driving, looking for a doctor's office that was open late. They found one in an office above the Belmont Theater. Not exactly a high-end operation, but it had to do. With the blood samples drawn and resting in Marge's purse, they had to wait until the next morning to spring into action. It was a long, anxious night.

At first light, Marge had her assignment: Get the blood samples to the Board of Health and get their approval. She was there at 8 a.m., when the office first opened, but was immediately hit with cold water. "Sorry, lady, we can't do blood samples until 4 p.m." Marge cried, "But we need them *now*! My future husband is being inducted into military service at 3 p.m. We can't wait that long!" The response, so typical of government agencies, was: "Sorry. That's just the way it is."

Marge caught Wes by telephone as he was clearing out his desk at Electronics Communication Equipment Company (ECEC) with the bad news. Wes told Marge to stay there, just outside the Board of Health; he would call her back shortly. ECEC had done plenty of work for the City of Chicago, and it was now time to call in some expedited favors. ECEC's corporate attorney was John O'Connor Fitzgerald, who was a relative of the Fitzgerald side of the Kennedy Family (as in Joe, Jack, and Bobby Kennedy). Wes walked into the attorney's office and explained the situation. While Wes talked, Fitzgerald started working the telephone:

"Herman? This is Fitz. Oh, I'm fine. I've got a favor to ask. At the Board of Health Office right now is a young woman; her name is Marguerite Aldridge. She is waiting to have a blood test run so that she and her fiancé can get married. He must report for induction into the military by 3 p.m. today. What can you do?" Herman said, "I'll take care of it. Tell her to wait there."

Marge waited as instructed. Forty minutes later, the waiting room door to the Health Office opened. A man stepped out with the Health Certificate and a questioning expression that clearly telegraphed, "Who the hell are you, that can get something like this done on the spur of the moment?!" She grabbed it and was off like a shot.

Next stop for Wes and Marge was a trip to City Hall for the marriage license, but they hit another snag: the line at the office was around the block. So many returning GIs, by the thousands, were likewise wanting to get married. Now what?

Fitz again came to the rescue. He instructed Wes: "Don't just stand there. Go to booth number two; knock three times on the back door and tell them who you are!"

Wes did as instructed. He went to the door and knocked three times. A little panel slid open, and a pair of eyes looked out. Wes said, "I'm Schum. Got a license for me?" The pair of eyes asked, "What kept you?" The license poked out of the slot, followed by, "That will be two bucks." Wes handed over the two bills, the panel door closed, and the couple had their marriage license!

By this point, it was 11:30 a.m. What seemed like an eternity had passed, but there was far more to do. Their next stop was likewise greased by Fitz, to the Office of the Chief Justice for the City of Chicago. His name was Scheffler. The pair knocked on his office door and a booming voice called out, "Who is it?" Wes responded, "Schum." Scheffler replied, "What kept you?"

Wes and Marge on their wedding day

By noon, they were finally married.

Fitz's magic was not finished just yet. He was also at the chief justice's office. There, he picked the couple up and off they went to the Bismarck Hotel to a party he had quickly arranged. The ECEC department heads were there, people from Cover Dual, family, and lifelong friends...even the pair of eyes who gave them the marriage license showed up. How Fitz pulled all that together for the Schums with virtually no notice was then, as it is now, mind boggling.

Perhaps it helped, being related to the Kennedys!

At 2:30 p.m., off they rushed to the train station. Right on schedule and with no time to spare, Wes Schum said a tearful goodbye to his new bride at 3 p.m., became a private in the Army, and embarked on a new adventure in life while Marge rode back home on the streetcar with her parents, wondering what would come next.

In retrospect, and thinking about what I've learned through Wes during our long association and friendship, this is so typical. His level of confidence in solving any problem and meeting any challenge is nothing like I've ever seen, and probably unlike what most anyone else has seen. What others might view as failure, Wes Schum merely observed as unscheduled detours along the journey to success. He unknowingly followed Winston Churchill's thoughts on achieving success to the letter.

Chapter 6: In the Army Now

The train ride was not terribly long, and soon Wes arrived at an induction center in the middle of nowhere. He and his fellow inductees next got on a bus; a bit later, they found themselves at Fort Sheridan in Lake County, Illinois. Arrival was just in time to get a round of shots, bedrolls, and some food. Here, for the next many weeks, these recruits got a steady diet of 5 a.m. rousting, physical conditioning, and endless drills—the whole basic training gig.

After two months, Wes was seriously homesick for Marge. Their sum total of time together, post marriage ceremony, was three celibate hours. This weighed heavily on Wes and so, a plan was formulated. As time progressed Wes found himself doing guard duty, four hours on and four hours off, for a period of 48 hours. Then he was off for 24 hours, and the routine repeated. While on duty, he was to carry an official looking briefcase. It was a rather nice-looking case, but it contained no papers. Why? Who knows? It was the Army way.

There was nothing required of Wes during his 24 hours off duty. It was a lot of spare time to hang around, and that got him to thinking.

At the end of one uneventful 48-hour stint, Wes went to his unit sergeant and said, "Sarge, here's five bucks and my telephone number. I'm going home. I have a brand-new bride waiting for me and we've never… We just held hands after the ceremony. I'm going. Call me if I must be back for anything. If not, don't call. Either way, I'll be back for my next forty-eight-hour assignment."

Wes in the Army

Sarge put the five bucks in his pocket and looked away. Wes took his cue. Empty but official looking briefcase in hand, off he walked toward the main gate, saluting as he went.

No orders. No pass. No nothin'.

Soon he was settled in on the electric train ride back to Chicago. He wasn't alone. MPs were on the train too, checking for guys who were AWOL. A pair of them had started at the train's last car and were steadily moving forward, one car at a time. It was a long train, but the ride was long, too. After a couple of hours, Wes could see them through the rail cars coming up the aisle. In another 15 minutes, they were entering the next car back. Wes was on the first car right behind the engine. It was getting close—uncomfortably close—but so was Wes. He jumped off at the next stop, on Belmont Avenue. From there he walked a short distance to the doctor's office where Marge was working as a medical assistant. Marge had no idea what Wes had conjured up and was ill-prepared to see him walk through the office door in uniform. They embraced and quickly headed to his family home for their important, unfinished wedding night business.

Wes and Marge

Retracing his steps, Wes took the train back, walked through the main gate, saluted everyone in sight, and clocked in with Sarge for his scheduled 48-hour guard shift, 30 minutes early. A few weeks later, Wes was shunted off to Camp Crowder, Missouri and the Army's mission for him became a bit clearer: Wes Schum would become a prisoner interrogator, among other things.

At Camp Crowder, Wes was fed a 4-month diet of prisoner interrogation and spy craft. Four hours a day were devoted to studying the Russian language. Prisoners the US, via Wes Schum, would be interrogating would likely be Russian—although we had just fought a war side by side with the Russians. He was given instruction on the planting of surveillance microphones, use of automatic weapons, demolition and the planting of bombs, the design and field-manufacture of improvised bombs, telephone wiretapping, finger printing and print analysis, and photography. And, how to kill an enemy in multiple ways, of course.

With training at Camp Crowder done, the next stop was senior level counter-intelligence training at the Holabird Signal Depot in Baltimore, Maryland. Word was that Wes' next assignment after Holabird would be overseas, in Korea.

Things were getting serious.

Marge had followed Wes while undergoing training in Illinois and Missouri, but the trip to Maryland was a bridge too far. They had a baby on the way, due in December 1946, and Wes wanted to be on hand. He had to find a way out of Korea, and fast.

(You know he did.)

Holabird's base commander, Colonel M. C. Nobel, enjoyed making speeches as part of the weekly pass in review parade activities. To do so, the colonel used a public address system with speakers spread throughout the parade grounds. One Saturday morning, it had heavily rained the night before and large puddles were still standing on the parade ground. Colonel Nobel gave this no mind and with shoes slightly in water touched the microphone to his lips.

Nothing was heard.

People were looking at him expectantly, but the colonel was just standing there. Someone soon figured out he was being electrocuted and knocked the microphone from his hands. The nearly fried man then collapsed and was carted off.

This was the opportunity Wes had been praying for. On Monday morning, he entered the commanding officers' building and requested a meeting with Colonel Nobel as soon as possible. The colonel's gatekeeper brushed him aside. Wes returned the next day and received the same brush off. On the third day, Wes was ready and cited section and verse of military law regarding why he, as an enlisted man, should be allowed a moment to speak to the colonel.

Not really knowing as much as he should about military legal matters, the gatekeeper relented and Wes was ushered in. Standing at attention, Wes waited for what seemed an eternity. Finally, the colonel put down his pen, looked up and barked, "All right, Schum; you are *persistent*! What do you expect me to do for you?"

From there, the conversation followed a path the CO did not expect, something like this:

"Nothing, sir. It is what I can do for you."

"For me? Really? What could that possibly be?"

"I saw how you were nearly electrocuted on the parade grounds this past weekend. I can fix the base's equipment so that will never happen to you again."

"You know how to do this?"

"Yes sir. I was deferred during the war to design and manufacture electronic products for the military. I know what to do and how to do it. I just need the parts from the supply section."

"How long will this take?"

"If you give me permission to secure the parts I need, the work will be done before next week's field inspection."

"OK, Schum. Let's see if you can deliver."

The colonel then jotted a note on his stationary, handed it to Wes, and said, "Take this to the supply office. They will get what you want. If they give you any crap, come back here and I'll take care of it...and them."

Wes got no crap, but he did get all the parts he had requested. His work was soon finished. He installed polarized power sockets on the electrical boxes in the parade field and corresponding polarized plugs on the public address amplifiers. He ensured the microphone cables were properly shielded, transformer-isolated, and bonded to ground for safety. He tested his work, barefoot and standing in water. No shocks, not even a tickle. He was ready.

Back at the colonel's office, Wes announced he was ready to test with the colonel. Out came the colonel onto the parade field, standing in water...but reluctant to touch the microphone. The memory of his painful shock had stuck in his mind. "Not to worry, sir." Wes grabbed the microphone, touched it to his lips and repeated his prior tests, again as the guinea pig. The colonel's eyes grew wide. He then grabbed the microphone from Wes, touched the microphone himself while repeating the tests, and broke into a wide grin.

"Schum, that PA system has knocked me on my ass for years, and no one has been able to fix it! *Damned* good job!"

Wes was feeling solid about himself after that and planning out his strategy on how to ask for a Korea-type favor when Colonel Nobel sent a courier out to offer an invitation to dinner at the colonel's residence.

Here we go.

Waiting for Wes at Colonel Nobel's dinner table was a huge steak, prepared by a German POW chef. It was succulent, and irresistible. Wes had eaten only Army chow for months, so a premier steak had his taste buds on high alert. After dinner, the colonel got down to business. "Schum, I got that big Stromberg-Carlson console radio in the living room as a gift from Congress while stationed in Cuba. It doesn't work... So, could you look at it?"

It was indeed big; the thing was nearly six feet long!

"Sir, I'll need some test equipment and parts from the base electronics shop. Could you assign me there and I'll see what can be done?"

"Consider it done, Schum. Report there in the morning, eight a.m. This radio will be waiting for you."

Wes was there at 8 a.m. on the dot...and so was the enormous radio. The fix was a simple one, luckily. He quickly found where the antenna coils on the broadcast and shortwave bands each had open primary windings, likely caused by the lightning storms that are typical throughout the Gulf Coast region. The big Stromberg radio was summarily repaired, and playing away at the colonel's residence that evening by 7 p.m.—just in time for steak dinner number two.

While working through his second succulent steak in a week, Wes informed the colonel of some deficiencies at the electronics shop, in particular how poorly trained its personnel were in troubleshooting and repairing equipment.

The bait was cast; would the Colonel bite?

He bit, all right, and hard!

"So Schum, could you fix that? Could you develop a training program, organize the shop, and get our men to actually fix our gear?"

"Yes, sir. But it would take time I don't have. You see, I'm supposed to ship out to Korea in a few weeks."

A few minutes passed, then the colonel said, "Schum, I need you here. Korea can take care of itself. I'll get your orders changed. So, do we have a deal?"

"Sir, if you need me here, I'm here!"

And so, Wes Schum didn't go to Korea. He would be on-scene for the birth of daughter number one, Gayle, who was to be the start of a continuing series that ended with daughter number four.

Now, safely tucked away at the base electronics shop, three things happened. First, he was elevated in 30-day increments from private to sergeant. Next, he developed a comprehensive set of training aids and held classes for entry-level technicians while also teaching electronics counter-intelligence classes. Lastly, his free time was spent in designing improved audio amplification systems for the base, which involved the actual study of hearing and ways to overcome hearing loss. At the back of his mind, though, was how to get rid of those damned AM heterodynes for whenever the amateur radio service was restored, post-war.

Years later, when distortion had been successfully removed from music radio stations as well as ham radio service, it came back to haunt Wes. When his daughters (and Marge!) would listen to rock music on the radio, he would put his hands over his ears and shout "I can't believe I spent years getting the distortion out of things, and people are putting it right back in on purpose!"

One of the problems Wes observed with the parade field public address, as well as other audio systems used on base, was the wide variation of audio levels produced by the loudspeakers or on base intercom systems. What was needed was an audio compression scheme that delivered clean, consistent-level audio with good articulation and low distortion. Clamping circuits had been devised in the past but those usually introduced high levels of distortion, making the amplified voice or music "mushy-sounding," lacking in clarity.

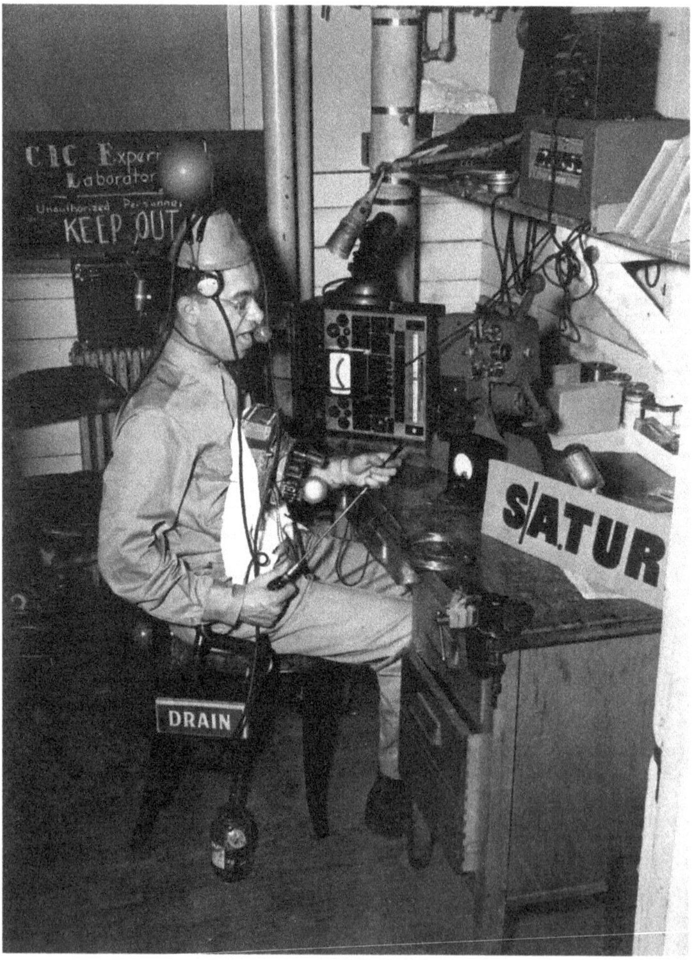

Wes blowing off steam at base

So, in his after-hours workshop, Wes began experimenting with different types of audio compression schemes that were fast-acting and designed with an eye toward least objectional distortion. He stumbled on an idea to provide a gating function whereby background noise would be "gated off," thereby making the pauses between spoken passages quiet—even in areas of moderate background noise. Eventually, this work gave way to a Schum-crafted gated compression amplifier and a US patent.

The gated compressor, as well as the addition of negative feedback and separate bass and treble controls, were installed within some spare public address amplifiers and tested on the base parade ground. The improvement in audio clarity was immediately apparent. Eliminating the heavy, energy-wasting bass and sharpening the system's treble response made the system sound bright and clean. Wes' modifications were extended to other audio and intercom systems on base as well. He was making Colonel Nobel look good...*really* good. Wes continued to refine his gated compressor scheme for what he hoped would become his first product as a civilian.

That's not all. While in the counter intelligence center, Wes had access to electronic device and research studies that were censored and restricted from mainstream publication. Those involved experiments and actual test results from a radio communications technology called single sideband. Single sideband was not new to the telephone industry, as it had been mathematically derived by AT&T research scientist John Carson in 1915 (patent granted in 1923[1]). Over the years, the technique was refined as a potential means of multiplexing more conversations (voice or data/teletype) over wired telephone trunk circuits.

Eventually, the technique was used to enhance high frequency radio links between the United States, England and some highest level/highest security military command needs. Its most important application during the war was in supporting multiple, simultaneous teletype data communications via a single voice radio channel. Since single sideband occupied half the bandwidth of an equivalent AM signal, it allowed AT&T significant capacity and noise reduction advantages over other transoceanic means.

1 See US Patent #1449382.

Those advantages and others clearly piqued Schum's interest, driving him to search out and read everything he could on single sideband. In his mind, he began to appreciate how this modulation/demodulation process could be applied to amateur radio, helping resolve the problem of AM heterodyne interference and expanding the capacity of ham radio's spectrum allocations.

Being drafted turned out to be a bit of good fortune for Wes. It gave him pause to *imagineer*[2] (to both imagine and to engineer) and the resources to develop commercial product ideas. Behind that base electronics shop, you see, was an enormous pile—more like a mountain, really—of broken or surplus electronics, parts ripe for the picking by an enterprising ham. Another bit of good fortune came Wes' way in December of 1946 along with the birth of his daughter, Gayle: a newly approved option for servicemen to leave the Army early.

By the end of the war in August 1945, there were over 12.2 million service members in the US military, with over 7.6 million stationed overseas. The public had tired of the war, not to mention the servicemen fighting it. The human cost being so incredibly and hurtfully large, coupled with the sacrifices made at home, demanded a rapid military drawdown.

The military's original demobilization plans for a gradual drawdown were essentially scrapped due to public outcry and new processes engaged in December 1946. Congress was getting hammered by those on the home front as well as in-field servicemen to draw down, and do it quickly. In the public's eyes, the time for continued US sacrifice was over. To illustrate the scope and speed of the military's revised decommissioning plan, by July 1947, the military's total enrollment was reduced by nearly 90%. Soon, the war's serviceman draft program was officially terminated.

Wes and Marge's new baby gave him an unexpected opportunity to return to civilian life, compliments of the US Congress, and he took it.

---

2 A most appropriate term cited from published author and longtime Ham Radio friend, Michael LeBoeuf, K5ML. Refer to his book, *Imagineering*.

On January 3rd of 1947, Wes Schum found himself deep in thought while barreling toward Chicago on a train. With 200 bucks of "mustering out" money and an official-looking briefcase packed full of product ideas by his side, the budding entrepreneur found himself in a scene right out of "October Sky." How was he to tell his dad that he didn't want to take over the family business of rolling cigars, but would rather be an electrical engineer instead. Following a lengthy and sometimes tearful discussion upon his return home, he was given his dad's blessing and was ready to embark on another new adventure in life.

Marge, Wes, and Gayle Schum

Chapter 7: Wes Electronics, in Chicago, IL

Ham Radio was back in action, with the conclusion of the War. The time to deal with those AM heterodynes plaguing amateur radio on a widespread basis had come. Several techniques to improve the effectiveness of radio telephony were under study by universities, engineers, and radio amateurs alike, just prior to and during the War. Techniques such as heterodyne elimination[3], better channel efficiency via single sideband, and higher voice security through speech inversion each had roles, albeit limited, during the war.

Understanding the value of the amateur radio service and its lab-like access to the HF spectrum as the War wound down, some had visions of potential commercial opportunities for those initially complex and costly technologies. Many believed that with further research and refinement, one could find wartime technology beneficial to peacetime interests.

One technology stood tall as having the best shot of resolving AM's heterodyne interference, thereby achieving spectrum efficiency: single sideband. It got the full attention of researchers at Stanford University, engineers at General Electric, the American Radio Relay League...

3 An important invention to minimize AM heterodyne interference was developed in 1941 by Mr. J. L McLaughlin and granted patent 2,364,863: the heterodyne eliminator. The device resultant from this patent was one utilized fully by the Federal Communications Commission, was published in QST Magazine, and saw field use in WWII.

and garage-based entrepreneurs like Wes Schum. Yet being freshly discharged by the US Army, with a new family and no immediate source of income, Wes had far more pressing priorities than ham radio or single sideband. Number one on his list was getting home fast and fueling an income stream. Maybe his work in gated compression and extremely low distortion audio amplifiers could solve an altogether different problem?

Marge was working as a medical assistant for a general practitioner whose young child had a hearing disorder. The girl was enrolled in a school for the deaf, and as one might imagine, she was having difficulty in language skills. While she could hear sounds, what she heard was very weak, muffled, and confusing. Her progress was steady, but agonizingly slow. On the train home, Wes wondered if he could help the girl and others like her. Solving difficult problems was what he was born to do, it seemed.

Once settled in Chicago, Wes made his way to the Ephpheta School for the Deaf, then located at 3150 N. Pulaski Road. There, he met with the school's superintendent, Anna Savoie, to learn more about how children with hearing disorders were treated, and if anything he had done to this point in his career could help them. Miss Savoie explained that those who were fully deaf were taught sign language, and those with some degree of treatable hearing disorders were enrolled in audible language labs. Sadly, most of the school's students were in the profoundly deaf category, and the language lab was ineffective for them.

Wes then toured the labs and viewed the type of equipment then in use. It was made by the Jay L. Warren Company, a local Chicago firm, and consisted of what appeared to be a set of record turntables, an audio amplification system, and a set of customized student desks. Each desk was equipped with headphone jacks. The students would don headphones like those used for radio reception and would listen to passages selected by the teacher. Since students often progressed at different rates, multiple record turntables having different lesson plans were operated by the teacher.

Language lab for children

Being curious, Wes parked at a student desk, donned a set of headphones, and asked to hear a lesson. While the audio he heard was usable for a person with average hearing, he wondered if the level was high enough and the audio produced clear enough to be effective. To him, it sounded excessively bassy and muddled. What might work for a person with some hearing loss might not work for someone who could hear virtually nothing. Days later he was back at the school at his own expense, making level versus frequency response measurements and observing student reactions to the sounds heard, if anything.

To him, it didn't appear the children could hear much of anything. Worse, the kids looked lost and disinterested. They were smart enough to sense that whatever the teachers were doing for them wasn't working.

There was no look of school revolt, only one of universally sad resignation.

Back home, in his workshop, Wes wondered if much higher audio level was a possible first step to an answer. Since the kids couldn't hear, maybe the problem was excessive attenuation that the Warren equipment could not effectively overcome. To test the concept, he next constructed a variable level, low-distortion amplifier add-on for the Warren system that was capable of a 140 decibel (140dB) sound level above ambient noise. To a person with normal hearing, such a level could cause hearing damage. But what about those who can't hear at all? A week's worth of tests showed he was onto something. Some of the children who previously could hear nothing perked up as they started hearing something as the level was increased above 110dB.

Next, he wondered if the headsets needed improvement. At the higher audio levels, the headsets began sounding harsh and somewhat distorted. Off to the local radio parts emporiums he trotted, in search of better headphones. He quickly discovered they were all like the Warren ones, meaning equally bad when driven to high levels. Eventually, he stumbled upon a supplier who had just received some miniature permanent magnet speakers that were not much larger than the transducers used on typical headsets. Just maybe...

Armed with a set of those miniature speakers and rubber-like earmuffs, Wes made up a homebrewed headset. It sounded fantastic! Off he went back to Ephpheta School for more student tests. The kids loved them; what were just noises before had become clear, distinct sounds. Back to the parts store to get enough speakers for four headsets he went. Then back to the school, for more tests and tweaks to the amplifier's frequency response (bass and treble). Soon, not only were the four sample students hearing sounds, in short order they were *imitating* what they heard.

Wes Schum was onto something big. Mr. Warren of the Jay L. Warren Company saw an opportunity. He needed to meet Schum, and fast. Wes knew little of the Warren Company and Jay Warren knew next to nothing of Schum, but both figured they could benefit from an association. Clearly, this young man had good instincts and ideas.

The Jay L. Warren Company had been in the language lab equipment business for a few years by that time. While not a startup, it was not far from one. The company didn't manufacture its equipment; for that it relied on outside job shops. Even Warren's design needs were farmed out to area subcontractors. Jay Warren wondered if Schum would consider designing equipment for him and by doing so, perhaps getting the jump on language lab competitors.

What Warren had in mind was right up Schum's alley.

Wes had already made up his mind that the only company he would be employed by would be his own: Wes Electronics, or something like it. Contract design and manufacturing worked well for Cover Dual and ECEC, so why not for him? A deal was struck between the two men and Wes Schum was in the audio and language laboratory business.

The union of the two provided highly beneficial to Wes. Jay Warren was older than he and had been in other businesses prior to this. His experiences served as a useful backstop to Wes, who could focus on pure engineering and product manufacturing. For the manufacturing part, once again Wes plucked his best associates who had worked with him at Cover Dual and ECEC. Roy Sherman and Nick Fishik were the first to be lured in, Roy for his manufacturing mind and Nick for his model-making craftsmanship. Others soon followed, as we'll see.

Once the ink dried on the Wes-Warren working agreement, the team circled back to the equipment at the Ephpheta School. Configuration changes were made to accommodate Wes' high-level power amplifier. A new wrinkle added to the Warren-Schum amplifier system was Wes' gated compression scheme. Since the audio levels needed to reach the children were so incredibly high, having a way to prevent level overshoot would be important. The gated compressor was still a product idea under development, but it could accomplish instantaneous level moderation. Plus, each new iteration was getting closer to the system's ultimate performance as envisioned possible by Wes. Nick Fishik crafted a more refined set of prototype headsets, and more tests at Ephpheta were soon undertaken.

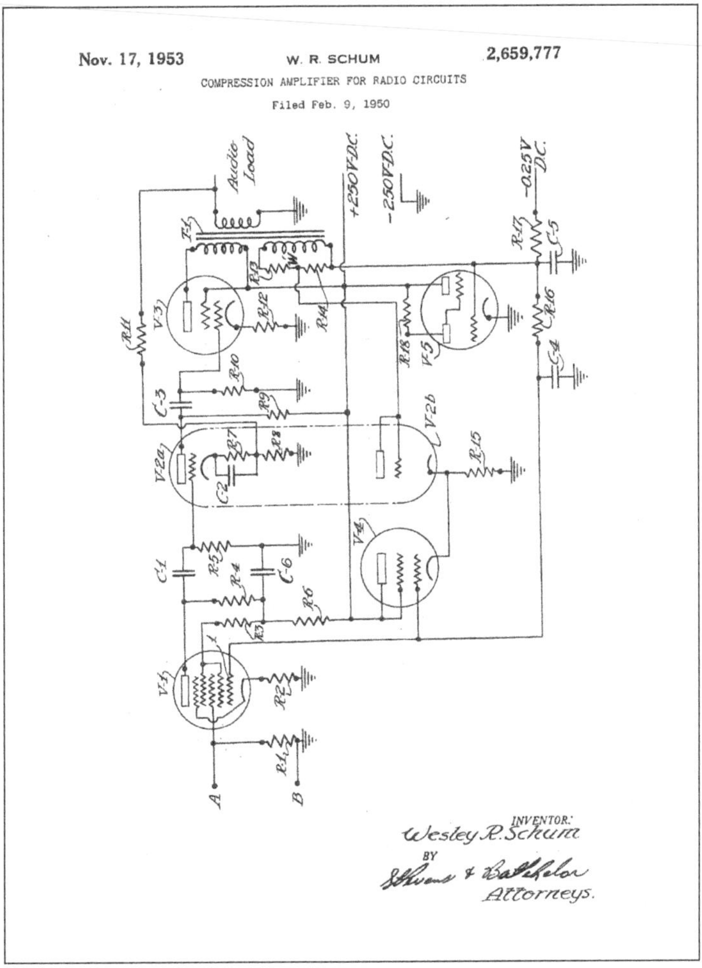

US Patent 2,659,777 Gated Compressor

They had clearly hit the jackpot.

News stories about hearing breakthroughs at the Ephpheta School became widely known. On Friday October 15, 1948 the *Chicago Daily Tribune*, the *Chicago Sun Times*, *Chicago Daily News*, and *Chicago Herald American* broke exciting stories with photographs of children hearing human voices for the first time. Headlines stating "20 Children Hear for the 1st Time;" "Just to Hear...It's Wonderful, Really;" and "Curtain of Silence Lifted for Kids" were the big news of the day.

Jay and Wes were hugging themselves, far beyond relieved. They had put all the markers on this work, and it paid off. The Jay L. Warren

Company was soon exploding at the seams with equipment orders. Wes had found the financial security niche he needed.

Just as the two were feeling a bit giddy about their success, a house painter brought them both back to Earth.

The Ephpheta School continued to assist Wes as he worked to refine his equipment ideas. During one on-site session, Wes noticed a painter diligently working in the next room. It was apparent he was hard of hearing; the man seemed to be deaf as a post. They had never tried their equipment on profoundly deaf adults, since the school was one for children. The two men wondered if a new market might exist. So, they asked permission to have the painter's hearing evaluated, using the children's lab gear.

Soon the painter was headphoned up and the test started, with Wes at the controls. Wes was growing more and more excited, as the man was clearly hearing the sounds, likely for the first time. At the conclusion of the sound tests, and through a sign language interpreter, Wes struck up the following conversation with the man.

'*Sir, could you hear sounds today?*'

'*Yes.*'

'*Were they clear sounds?*'

'*Yes.*'

'*Please put the headphones back on.*'

The man did as requested.

'*Now, sir, I am speaking to you. Can you hear me?*'

'*Yes.*'

'*Great! Now that you can hear sounds and even my voice, would you wish to be enrolled in hearing and speech classes?*'

'NO!'

Wes was floored. All the children who had heard for the first time were eager to enroll in classes. After recovering from this unforeseen setback, Wes asked, in disbelief, '*Why not?!*'

After a lengthy pause, the man calmly responded, '*I am a painter. I paint houses for a living. I don't hear people complain about my work. I don't hear dogs barking. I don't hear my wife's nagging. I like it that way!*'

Fortunately for the Jay L. Warren and Wes Electronics Companies, the next group of hearing-impaired adults tested felt much differently!

The Warren-Schum association continued for nearly thirty-five years, Wes designing and supplying Warren various models of language and speech therapy systems. Jay Warren so strongly believed in Wes that as he embarked on ideas for radio communications in late 1949, Warren became the new fledgling company's principal investor and stockholder. That company?

Central Electronics.

Warren's wired language lab systems gradually gave way to low-frequency induction types and then to the Walk-Away, which used multichannel FM equipment. These were each manufactured by Central Electronics, even when ownership transitioned to Zenith Radio and, ultimately by Schum Electronics, Inc. once Zenith exited its amateur radio business.

But that's getting ahead of the story.

Girls hearing for the first time via Wes-Warren equipment

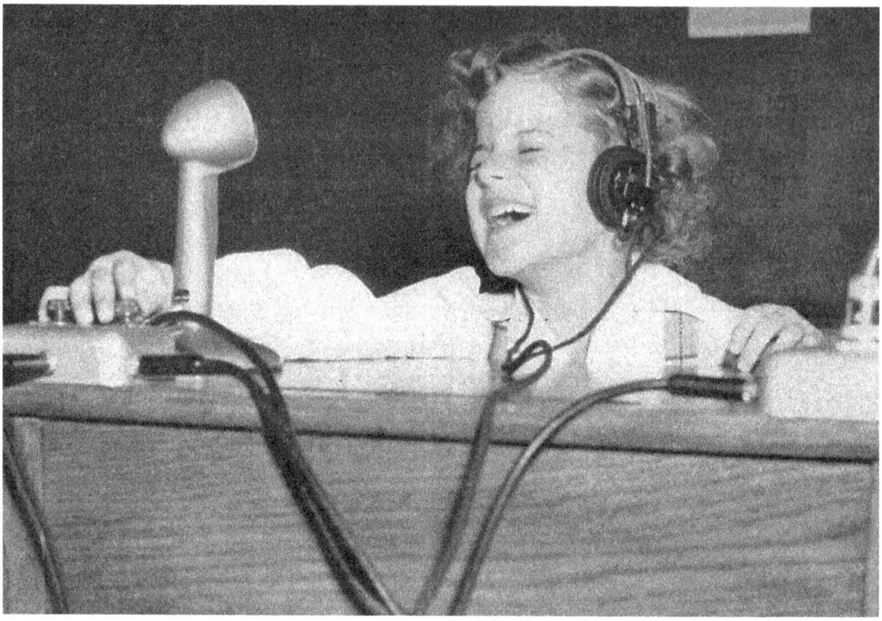

Girl hearing for the first time

Warren T-1 Trainer with Schum headset

Chapter 8: Single Sideband

While Wes was getting his feet on the ground in Chicago and getting his new family's financial house in order, a small but steadily growing group of university professors and engineers began experimenting with single sideband via amateur radio. It is one thing to develop a technology in a lab, but it is an altogether different story to test that theory in real-world settings. And there is no better test bed than the broad frequency spectrum granted to radio amateurs, who by their very nature are all-in when it comes to experimentation.

It stands to reason that the first of such post-war ham band experiments would be conducted via a university amateur radio club. That is exactly what happened; the first on-air amateur radio experiments using single sideband were those with equipment designed by university professor Oswald (Mike) Villard (W9QYT) and operated by students at Stanford University's club station (W6YX). The first two-way amateur sideband contact was on September 21st, 1947. It occurred on 3970kHz at 9:30PM (PST) between the club station and Winfield Wagener (W6VQD). Others involved in early 1947 sideband experiments included Art Nichols (W0TQK), Lyle Knowles (W0NWF), Dave Thompson (W6VQB), Bob Beaudette (W7FXI), and Chet Carr (W6NVH).

Likewise, many others throughout New England were involved in single sideband study and experimentation—most notably Don Norgaard (W2KUJ), as both an amateur experimenter and engineering professional working for the General Electric Company.

In 2020, single sideband is the voice communications standard for HF radio communications in amateur, commercial, and military circles. And while there is a small resurgence of AM operation—principally by those who have restored vintage equipment and repurposed former AM broadcast equipment for 160 and 75 meters—single sideband is clearly the dominant voice mode. So, today's new amateur enthusiasts may not fully understand the differences between the two modes, or why the work done by those early sideband pioneers remains important, deserves admiration, and is of historic significance.

Perhaps the following will help in understanding more about AM and single sideband, which is but another form of amplitude modulation. Modulation is the ability of adding intelligence information onto a radio frequency signal. If the intelligence is in the form of voice/human speech, it is possible to change either the amplitude, frequency, or phase characteristics of a radio signal or carrier to impart such information. Prior to World War II, the principal media for voice communications on high-frequency channels (those between 3 and 30MHz) was via amplitude modulation.

The process of amplitude modulation creates two side frequencies or sidebands adjacent to, above and below, the radio carrier signal. As an example, if a carrier signal was positioned at 3500kHz and was modulated by a 1kHz tone, the process of modulation would generate two new signals: one signal located 1kHz above the carrier frequency, and one signal located 1KHz below the carrier frequency. In this case, 3499kHz would be the lower signal, 3500kHz the carrier, and the upper signal would be at 3501kHz. If the modulating signal was a band of frequencies rather than one, then the information would then be contained in two bands of information, sidebands, above and below the carrier signal.

The interesting thing is that the speech information contained in either sideband is identical: the same information. And so, if the modulating speech signal has a bandwidth of 3kHz, then the actual transmitted amplitude modulated signal would span 6kHz in width.

That's not all. Assuming a 100-watt AM transmitter that is 100% modulated, the power in the carrier would be 100 watts and 50 watts of audio power, total, in the two sidebands - or only 25 watts in each. Keep in mind, communications effectiveness is that within the sidebands. Since both sidebands contain the exact-same information, if it were possible to eliminate both one of the two sideband and the carrier and then repurpose the transmitter's full power into that remaining *single* sideband, two obvious objectives would be met. First, the transmitted signal's bandwidth would be essentially cut in half, and secondly, the power that would have been used to generate the carrier signal and other sideband could then be applied to just one. All things considered, single sideband operation offers as much as a 9dB communications advantage as compared to double sideband AM.

From a purely communications standpoint, single sideband has significant operational and QRM-fighting advantages over AM. Perhaps the best of those is the elimination of heterodyne beat notes due to closely spaced carriers associated with AM signals. That is, if a ham operator is listening to one AM station, but a second station begins to be heard due to changing signal propagation, and that station is 1kHz removed in operating frequency, the operator will hear an annoying 1kHz beat tone that will materially disrupt one's ability to hear the desired voice information. If other AM signals are close and within the receiver's passband, depending on carrier spacings, more heterodyne beat tones will be heard. Where one offending AM signal can produce one heterodyne beat response, two offending signals can produce *three*! Three offending but tightly packed signals can produce *five*. Yikes!

A band crowed with AM signals can thus degenerate into a beat note polluted frenzy.

This doesn't happen too frequently today, since the number of AM stations operational at any given time on the Amateur bands are few; most all are operating single sideband. But in the 1940s and 1950s, when double-sideband AM was the primary voice communications mode and hundreds of stations could be active on any crowded ham band, it was an absolute heterodyne madhouse (think Channel 19 CB Radio in the 1970s). If a ham radio station didn't have a *huge* signal, its operator had better acquire a good CW fist, a new-found interest in stamp collecting, or both.

So, how exactly is the redundant sideband eliminated? As it turns out, it can be eliminated in brute-force fashion by filtering, or it can be eliminated using the more elegant signal cancellation approach, phasing. Each method has its pros and cons, as will become evident.

The filter method came first. Carson's 1915 single sideband experiments were at exceptionally low frequencies, well below today's broadcast band. In Carson's configuration, he essentially generated a traditional AM signal absent the carrier signal. Doing so involved a balanced modulator scheme that nulled the carrier while generating both upper and lower sidebands. Keep in mind, the frequency used to generate this double sideband/no carrier signal was exceptionally low: less than two hundred kilohertz (called cycles then). In fact, because the bandwidth of extremely low frequency antenna systems is so narrow, Carson viewed the antenna system as being a bandpass filter of sorts, one having enough selectivity to eliminate one sideband.

Pretty ingenious, when you think about it. The antenna then could do double duty as a signal radiator and sideband elimination filter. If the antenna's resonant bandwidth was properly positioned relative to the generated double-sideband signal, the desired sideband could be radiated at low loss while the other non-essential sideband was rejected. Unfortunately, Carson's system wasn't practical for long distance communications, as frequencies needed for consistently reliable transatlantic communications were considerably higher and the resultant antenna would no longer function as a sideband filter.

Making matters worse, constructing effective sideband elimination via filtering became more complex and expensive as frequency rose. So, while the sideband information could be generated at a lower frequency and mixed to a higher one, the sideband blocking filters became large and bulky. Until the mid-1940s, such filters were typically constructed using lumped inductor and capacitor elements, and the values necessary were large and often non-standard. Thus, sideband elimination filters were custom-made, bulky, and difficult to mass produce.

A less costly method for generating single sideband was sought and subsequently discovered by Ralph Hartley at Western Electric (AT&T)[4]. His method used mathematic-trigonometric relationships to eliminate the unwanted side band. Hartley's system used two balanced modulators. The carrier signal for one was shifted 90 electrical degrees relative to the other. Likewise, the modulating audio signal was shifted 90 degrees relative to each of the two balanced modulators. When the outputs of the two balanced modulators were then summed, the result was one sideband was reinforced in level while the other was 180-degree phase cancelled. To change the Hartley system to support the opposite sideband one had only to reverse the audio signal connections to the two balanced modulators.

The generation of two 90-degree shifted carrier signals was simple, since that portion of the system operated at a single fixed carrier frequency. The development of an audio phase shift network that would keep the phase difference constant across the audio (speech) bandwidth of 300 to 3500Hz was far more difficult and would take until wartime research and 1946 to resolve. In the December 1946 issue of *Electronics Magazine*, R.B. Dome—an engineer at General Electric— published "Wide Band Phase Shift Network," which described an all-pass audio network that could maintain a 90-degree phase shift over the speech range of 200–5000Hz. The Dome network used just a small number of inexpensive resistive and capacitive elements, thereby rendering the

4 Patent 1,666,206: Modulation System. Granted April 17, 1928.

phasing technique of generating single sideband signals at a lower cost compared to filter systems.

Once published by Dome, the last technical impediment to expanded single sideband use had been tackled. Using the phasing technique, a single sideband signal could be generated at any frequency, at reasonable cost, and with good performance. Over time, though, phasing networks would gradually change operational characteristics due to component aging, so phasing equipment required more maintenance as compared to filter-generation schemes. Until the cost of mechanical and crystal type filter elements dropped due to the standardization of intermediate signal generation frequencies in the late 1950s, and less costly means for manufacturing the necessary filter elements were developed, the phasing method became and remained popular.

By the early 1960s, a shift in manufacturing single sideband systems using the filter principal had occurred and phasing was again a hobbyist domain. However, as digital signal processing became widely available and low in cost compared to filters, single sideband could again be generated via the phasing principal.

So, what was once old had become "new" again.

While the above discussion of AM and single sideband sets the stage for what follows next, consider reading Appendix 1 to learn in more depth about how single sideband is generated via the phasing principals. Look also to the ARRL *Radio Amateurs Handbook* and now out-of-print but easily found issues of the ARRL's *Single Sideband for the Radio Amateur* for more information involving the theory associated with speech modulation formats, receivers, and transmitting equipment. Beware: once you start digging in and learning about the various methods of receiving, generating, and amplifying single sideband, you may find yourself spending a lot more time experimenting in *your* workshop, too!

Chapter 9: On the Air with Single Sideband

The use of single sideband on radio frequencies took two different development paths: a commercial one, geared toward military, maritime, and aircraft usage, plus the one embarked upon by amateur radio hobbyists. The military's interest in single sideband began in World War II and accelerated during the post-war period.

Many have written about the role of the Collins Radio Company and its work with the Air Force's Strategic Air Command (SAC). Collins' work during the Cold War was unprecedented, important and a process that accelerated single sideband's use. Yet those SAC experiments came after an important top-secret project undertaken by the Air Force in the post-war 1940s.

By this point in 1949–50, Wes Schum was involved in the manufacture of audio systems, but remained in close contact with Colonel Nobel at the Holabird Signal Depot. The colonel understood Wes' skills and the training programs he had established for the Base's electronics personnel. The colonel felt Schum could contribute as a training contractor on an important new communications project being undertaken by the Air Force, the Single Sideband Program. Keep in mind that during the war, the nation's Air Corps was an element branch of the US Army, thus the colonel's counter-intelligence unit was an included party in an interesting Airways and Air Communications Service directive.

Issued on April 28th, 1950 this directive gave notice of a single sideband training program that was to commence in parallel with the Air Force's commissioning of a multi-channel single sideband communications network. The directive goes on to say, "The Single Side-Band Program was initiated to meet the increased worldwide postwar circuit requirements. The program calls for the installation of multi-channel single side-band equipment at certain strategic locations to meet the demands of a USAF global communications system."

The project's equipment had been manufactured and field installation of this new system was underway at the time the directive was issued. "Sixteen (16) single side-band equipments will be made available for delivery in June 1950. Installation for the Washington-Pepperrell circuit is underway at this time." The directive, unfortunately, does not indicate the equipment's manufacturer but from available information, review of IRE Conference papers presented by Don Norgaard on single sideband transmission and receiving systems, the 1946 published work conducted by Dome on wideband all-pass phase shift networks, and by the 1948 announcement of the GE YRS-1 receiving system, the equipment manufacturer was likely the General Electric Company.

It wasn't the Collins Radio Company, since it had no significant single sideband equipment development programs underway in 1950. That work would come a bit later, as you'll see. What Collins' work later cemented was the importance of single sideband for aircraft communications and naval/maritime operations. Where GE had a jump on fixed site communications, Collins envisioned a broader need by the nation's highly mobile air/sea defense platforms.

1948 announcement of the GE YRS-1 receiving system

Hams wanted a piece of the sideband pie, too. It didn't take long before AMers began noticing some "Donald Duck-like" signals on the high end of 75 meters—the experiments being conducted by Stanford University hams in 1947. Likewise, the editors of *QST* and CQ magazine sensed the value of this new technology and the impact it could have on amateur HF communications.

The January 1948 issue of *QST* signaled the then-envisioned impact that single sideband would have on amateur radio and pointed to the important work being undertaken by curious ham experimenters:

"Several articles in this issue of our magazine point the way toward the most significant development that has ever occurred in amateur radiotelephony: carrierless single-sideband emission. After years of fearing that our receivers weren't stable enough to permit the use of S.S.S.C[5]—as we're calling it—the adventitious appearance on the air of an experimental station with this method of emission has shown that it isn't so difficult after all and that its merits are waiting for all of us. And so immense are these advantages that we are convinced that a speedy revolution in our equipment and operating practices is imminent and certain."

The League was not alone as the editors of CQ Magazine had been watching the progress of the Stanford University's tests with high interest, and followed closely the ground-breaking paper on single sideband presented by General Electric's Don Norgaard at the I.R.E. National Convention in March 1948. General Electric had sensed important military, maritime, and commercial opportunities if a viable sideband radiotelephone system could be brought to market. To be effective, single sideband's equipment had to be stable, as easy to operate as a traditional AM system, offer superior technical performance, and be reasonable in price.

CQ Magazine's approach to single sideband was more measured than the League's. CQ opined in its May 1948 issue:

"From time to time, articles have appeared extolling the virtues of a transmission system, but after a brief flurry of activity, interest wanes

---

5 Single Sideband, Suppressed Carrier or SSSC

and eventually even the most ardent proponents have placed it in the discard."

While the work at Stanford was clearly a step above with respect to thoroughness and experimentation, what likely changed the dynamic was the keen interest being place onto single sideband by the General Electric Company. Surely, if an enterprise as large and multifaceted as GE was pouring research dollars, time, and energy into sideband, then perhaps this one would stick and earn its place in telecommunications.

CQ's vision in May 1948 was far-reaching in that it correctly placed the burden of sideband's acceptance onto the manufacturing community. "As we see the situation now, it is up to the manufacturers. If practical equipment is made available to us before interest wanes, then single sideband should become popular, and eventually even supplant the conventional double sideband plus carrier system now used."

CQ would soon publish articles on the construction of filter-type sideband exciters and later followed the work of Don Norgaard's at home SSB, Jr. 75-meter exciter. *QST* had also gone all-in on sideband with a flurry of articles in 1948: "Selectable Single-Sideband Reception," "What about SSB," "A Single-Sideband Detector," "A New Approach to Single-Sideband," "Practical Single-Sideband Reception," and "A Simple Single-Sideband Transmitter".

With CQ and *QST* providing technical information to hams in measured steps and through constructable examples, home workshop experimentation began to take root. Fueling even more growth, the League invented a way to give its members a snapshot of what others had been doing in their workshops and on air by starting its new *QST* column *On the Air with Single Sideband.* Here it was easy for readers to chart sideband's experimental progress on the west and east coasts, and over time, throughout the Midwest and then all of the US.

As CQ's editorial staff had so correctly predicted, the success of single sideband would rest on the manufacturing community and its ability to design, construct, and market good, viable, and simple to use equipment.

That took time. Except for Westinghouse and General Electric, few major corporations were willing to make the needed product development and engineering investments. AM was the de facto HF voice communications standard used throughout the world. The radio industry was heavily invested in AM technology and designs that worked. AM might be a power hog and its bandwidth wide, but it did allow for usable voice communications. AM's equipment, both for transmission and reception, was simple and relatively straightforward to operate. So, the major firms were reluctant to rock the boat.

Isn't that so typical, though? When ground-breaking new technologies eventually find acceptance, it is often the case that small operations— those born in garages or at the kitchen table— are the ones to accelerate widespread acceptance. A startup has no investment in the old, traditional way of doing things. It has no legacy clients to be concerned about backward compatibility. A small startup opens with a clean slate. The two things most startups lack are money to sustain prolonged R&D and an established marketing program. Startups usually make do with bootstrapping themselves into relevancy; some make it...many don't.

By operating under competitive radar screens, if a large established corporation or industry lacks vision and resists change, it risks getting swept away by the surviving nimble, fresh-faced upstarts. The key, of course, is the upstart's drive to survive and that takes steely dedication, time, and a heavy dose of luck.

The generation of single sideband, in early experiments, initially took the brute-force approach of using bandpass filters to suppress the unwanted sideband. The problem was that filters capable of a flat bandpass and step skirt selectivity were complex to design and expensive to manufacture. To keep filter costs within some element of reason, it was necessary to construct those at low frequencies. To get a filter-based transmitter then operational at some fixed frequency in the 3 to 30MHz region meant the need for a multiple frequency conversion scheme. With each frequency conversion, there came the issue of spurious emissions that must be filtered out. And so, while on the surface generating sideband signals using the filter method was seemingly straightforward, it quickly became otherwise.

Perhaps such complexity could be accepted for fixed-channel commercial usage, but what about those services or operations who were allowed or expected to operate on multiple frequencies throughout many parts of the radio spectrum? It would be impractical to employ groups of individual transmission systems in such cases. One sideband signal generator should reasonably be capable of operating on many sets of frequencies in differing parts of the HF radio spectrum, which is what amateurs would want in their radio stations.

It is this which slowed the widespread acceptance of single sideband throughout amateur radio. But these obstacles in no way limited experimentation on first 75 meters and then 20 meters, albeit in a channelized fashion. On 75 meters, sideband activity eventually centered on 3999.5kHz lower sideband. By conducting tests at the high end of the band, interference to normal AM operations would be less likely. Conversely, the sidebanders would cause less interference and Donald Duck squawking to AM listeners—not that using 3999.5kHz dissuaded AM listeners.

To some, trying to copy those unusual sounding signals was itself a useful challenge. What were they saying? How did that sideband stuff work? How come those sideband signals sounded so broad when they are supposed to be so narrow? Why do I have to chase them around if they're operating crystal controlled? Could I do sideband? Why would I want to do sideband?

Other operators took a more sinister view of sideband and sidebanders, as its adopters were called. Letters to *QST* and *CQ* often lamented the audacity of sideband and viewed it as a threat. "You are making my station obsolete." "I have a small fortune invested in AM gear and what you are doing is gonna make it next to worthless." "This is my hobby… why should I be forced to scrap what has taken years to build?"

The comments voiced against amateur sideband were coming in hot and heavy, to the point that *CQ*'s beleaguered editor commented,

"All joking aside, if the response from many amateurs we've talked to is typical, it will be a long time before SSSC replaces anything. But it may well have an important place in ham radio, and we owe it to ourselves to give it every test."

To be sure, the adoption of amateur sideband faced a steep uphill battle. I'd bet discussions like these went on while vacuum tube oscillators and power amplifiers replaced spark gap transmitters, too. None of us reading this book were around for that technology upheaval, but wouldn't the same arguments about spectrum efficiency and less interference (QRM) apply then, too? Generationally, people seem willing to accept change...if *they* don't have to change.

Keep in mind, most all this sideband work in the beginning years was done by experimenters: university engineering students and technical people who either worked in the post-war electronics field, or curious hobbyists with occasional time to spend on their pet project. Lacking a conclusive deadline, sideband development was moving along, but slowly. Weeks became months and then years. This slow pace gave the crowd against it time to solidify their opinions through letters to publications, vocally on air, and in some instances, physically, in person.

So, while sideband offered many good reasons for its rapid adoption by the amateur community, what was to keep it from winding up in the idea ash bin, as had many other promising and seemingly brilliant ideas before? Sure, if *everyone* adopted sideband, then anywhere from five to ten times the number of stations could be accommodated within the FCC's allowed phone band segments. Yet that was a *big if*, and took a lot of imagination to swallow in the late 1940s.

None of this escaped Wes Schum and a small handful of others who were looking beyond their sideband homebrews and thinking big...manufacturing big, too. To them, sideband presented a perfect opportunity for new startups.

The lure of being part of something new and technically important was irresistible. That phasing scheme Don Norgaard was promoting at the 1948 IRE Conference sure sounded good. Using General Electric's simplified phasing principle, a sideband signal could be generated at the actual operating frequency, something a filter rig was unlikely to do. Norgaard was also a ham (W2KUJ) and used his spare time to craft sideband ideas useful to other amateur experimenters.

The eventual fruits of Don's transmitter experiments, Sideband Jr. (SSB Jr.), were published in the 1950 November-December issue of *GE Ham News*. Don's companion sideband receiving converter was later described in the 1951 July-August issue of *Ham News*.

The SSB Jr. was conceived as an inexpensive, easily constructed 75-meter crystal-controlled rig. It developed a 5-watt output signal, plenty to drive a reasonably sized outboard linear amplifier. One could next build a linear power amplifier or change the bias on existing AM/CW rigs from Class C to Class B or AB linear operation.

Why a linear amplifier, as opposed to Class C? Simply put, the process of generating a single sideband signal is one of frequency translation. That is, the frequency components that make up band-limited, 300–3000Hz speech energy are translated up to a like band of radio frequencies. The amplitude and spacing of frequencies relative to each other in the band-limited speech band are preserved in the new RF-translated form. To prevent any unwanted signal distortion, it is imperative that those same amplitude and spectral relationships be maintained in all stages of the sideband generation process, including the final power amplifier—thus the need for high-quality linear signal amplification.

Class C amplifiers as used in AM and CW transmitters do not require that same degree of amplified signal purity for their transaction of information. In those instances, RF power amplifiers can be operated at higher efficiencies by providing pulses of amplified signal waveforms and then relying on the flywheel effect of the transmitter's output network (tank circuit) to reconstruct low distortion sine-wave energy.

Fixed frequency operation can be a hinderance (ask any rock-bound Novice licensee of the '50s and early '60s), especially as more sideband experimentation and casual operations ensued. Some ham shack experimenters had even conjured up variable frequency oscillators (VFOs) for their SSB Jr. versions and could shift frequency a bit in the 75-meter band...but not too far, as doing so would require tweaking of phase-shift adjustments to retain good unwanted sideband suppression.

Don's outboard sideband receiving converter likewise used the phasing principal and allowed one to listen to either sideband by a flick of a switch. Even AMers could benefit from adding a sideband converter onto their receiving equipment. Since the information in either sideband of an AM signal contains the same voice information, if an AM transmission's upper sideband was receiving interference, the operator could simply switch and listen to the lower one, often interference free.

Now, back to Wes Schum. While attention during normal business hours was laser-focused on the Jay L. Warren Company and earning a living, while at night and on weekends his ham radio interest shifted to single sideband. The many advantages of single sideband intrigued Wes, and so he constructed a filter rig to see first-hand how well sideband played in the ham band environment. As for the disadvantages... Well, those could be conquered in time using the Schum full speed ahead method.

His first actual on-air sideband experience was in mid-1949. There, he joined a growing crew of local experimenters on 3970kHz. Like all others, the immediate problem started and ended with the difficult sideband elimination filter. Beginning with the discrete LC approach, he built many different types and didn't like any of them. With each tried configuration, the opposite/upper sideband could be attenuated but in no way considered suppressed. He would need a multi-section filter stuffed in a shoebox to get enough of a steep-sided filter cutoff to write home about. Any QSO attempt at 3999.5kHz using one of those anemic filters would have been akin to waving a red cape in front of the FCC.

Perhaps the most important aspect of those early on-air experiments was the camaraderie it spawned. In those early days, everyone was eager to help and shared ideas freely. These on-air talents would spur each other on, congratulating each new success and collectively trying to figure out a fix for anyone's dilemma of the day.

The crowd soon figured that crystal lattice filters would provide the selectivity needed for good sideband suppression, but the cost for custom-made crystals was unattractively high. We are talking ham radio operators here, guys who instinctively seek the highest degree of performance for the absolute least cost. I'm not inferring that hams are notoriously tight-fisted when it comes to buying bits for their hobby... It's just that a goodly portion are known to have short arms and incredibly deep pockets, particularly while trolling a hamfest bone yard.

Once the nation's radio parts emporiums became flooded with inexpensive WWII surplus, hams descended like hungry locusts. Here, experimenters could find all sorts of useful electronic components for pennies—if they dug deep enough in the piles of electronic waste. Whoever was the first ham that spotted surplus quartz crystals while thinking about sideband filters and put those two ideas together is unknown. That person deserves a spot in the "Amateur Single Sideband Hall of Fame" as instantly the experimenter's filter problem was over. My vote goes to F. E. Edmunds, W1JEO. In his November 1950 *QST* article, "A Crystal-Filter SSB Exciter," Edmunds describes his use of surplus Signal Corps quartz crystals to fashion a 450kHz bandpass filter.

The W1EJO exciter developed sideband energy at a 450kHz IF level and heterodyned this using a mixer and 3.4–3.55MHz VFO to provide a 75-meter lower sideband signal, tunable between 3.85 and 4.0MHz. The importance of having a higher SSB IF channel at 450kHz, as opposed to early LC filter designs, was to eliminate one mixer stage and the problems multi-step mixer schemes present with respect to spurious signals. The crystals used were labeled *32.4MHz*, *36.2MHz*, and *32.3MHz*, which happened to be the operating frequencies for their intended equipment use—but they were ground to oscillate at 450.0kHz, 452.8kHz, and 448.6kHz.

How EJO figured that out is a mystery! Yet, the fact that these crystals were readily available and at extremely low cost suddenly had people building filter type sideband exciters.

Of course, Wes followed that wave (so to speak) and in quick time built several different filter exciters using surplus crystals to better evaluate and weigh their pros and cons. The filters were a godsend, as good opposite sideband suppression could be obtained with them, and eventually sideband experimental traffic migrated to the absolute band edge: 3999.5kHz. Doing so helped minimize the catcalls and noise from those disgruntled AMers who didn't fully appreciate this new mode's entry onto ham radio...yet.

But when Don Norgaard's Sideband Jr appeared in *GE Ham News*[6], Wes knew this was the answer. The principal problem with manufacturing filter type sideband rigs would be the cost and complexity of the filter. Using surplus crystals for an experimental radio was one thing, but could one be assured of a steady supply? And while 450kHz filters were OK for a single band rig, operation on multiple bands would require a double (or more) conversion scheme—going back to mixing problems again.

The phasing approach could have its signal generated on the actual operating frequency or any other frequency. So that meant Wes could choose a non-ham frequency—say, 9MHz—to generate a phasing-based sideband signal, and by using only one mixer stage operate both the 75- and 20-meter bands. That is, while using a 9MHz intermediate sideband signal, a 5MHz mixer reference could develop either a 4MHz (difference) or 14MHz (sum) response. And, if the mixer reference was not a crystal, but a VFO that tuned between 5.0 and 5.5MHz, his exciter's resultant sideband signal would be fully tunable—and more importantly, retain its suppression characteristics over both phone bands. The best part was that phasing required only low-cost resistive and capacitive elements to make the important audio 90-degree phase shift network. No custom crystals were needed.

6 See: SSB, Jr from the November/December 1950 issue of GE Ham News.

Wes knew this was the way to get sideband to amateur radio's masses.

His next step was to build several of these tunable phasing rigs and conduct exhaustive on-air tests to verify the packaged concept. Then, he passed a couple of cleaned up, early prototypes on to his best ham friends in Chicago for trial impressions.

The received comments were more than favorable. A business case for building a commercial sideband product for hams was beginning to take shape, but he soon had more questions than answers. How about a companion receiving converter? Then he could sell a complete, packaged system. Should he sell it with a parts kit rig, fully wired, or both? If fully wired, he'd need manufacturing help, and fast! How many parts should he order from suppliers? What suppliers, and when? What about instruction books, packaging, and advertising?

It all boiled down to money. How much would he need to start? Where would he get it? How soon could he expect to generate a cash flow of sold units? The primary item Wes needed was capital to build his new radio product, and so that was his next step.

Chapter 10: Central Electronics Is Born

When starting a new venture, most leave the thorniest issues to last, and money clearly ranks as a rather thorny one. Wes and Marge were no exception here. While Wes Electronics was fine for the specific amount of work being done locally for Jay L. Warren, that name just didn't convey the right message for a new ham radio operation. This was destined to become big, right?

Think nationwide!

Well... Chicago is pretty much located in the center of the USA. Marge suddenly suggested, "Why not *Central* Electronics?!" Wow! That's perfect! So, the new company had its name. Where to locate it? That part was easy; it would be operated out of the basement of the family home, at 2125 W. Giddings, which Wes had bought when he was 21 years old. No commuting problems to deal with, surely! Besides, that was where the design work for Jay L. Warren happened; why not start there? That was an easy decision to make, since Central Electronics had no finished products, no real ham customers, and—the biggest issue—no cash, as of yet. Wes would also need an antenna to test his creations, and one was readily available in the service alley...he used it every night, on 3999.5kHz.

And so it went; things gradually settled out. Wes and Marge built new work benches in the basement, added electrical wiring, and got things ready. One by one, the obstacles in starting the operation were resolved, except for the biggest one.

Oddly, that took care of itself.

Over the months needed to form Central Electronics, the two talked it up, non-stop, to their friends, family, and Jay Warren; Jay would often meet with Wes to discuss new language lab ideas. In Wes, Jay saw a sure thing. This guy was a brilliant dynamo and had no choice but to become successful. Sideband looked to be a wide-open market and a ground floor opportunity for the new company. Warren correctly sensed that with him becoming an invested member, then his access to Wes and the new company's anticipated expanded manufacturing capability would allow the Warren Company's hearing product line to grow with it. Of course, Leo Schum was more than ready to help his son, and the surprise interest by Jay Warren gave the startup its seed money to get the ball rolling.

By the time the various investment agreements had been signed and the new company duly registered in Delaware, Wes Schum had his sights on product number one. It would be called the Model 10A.

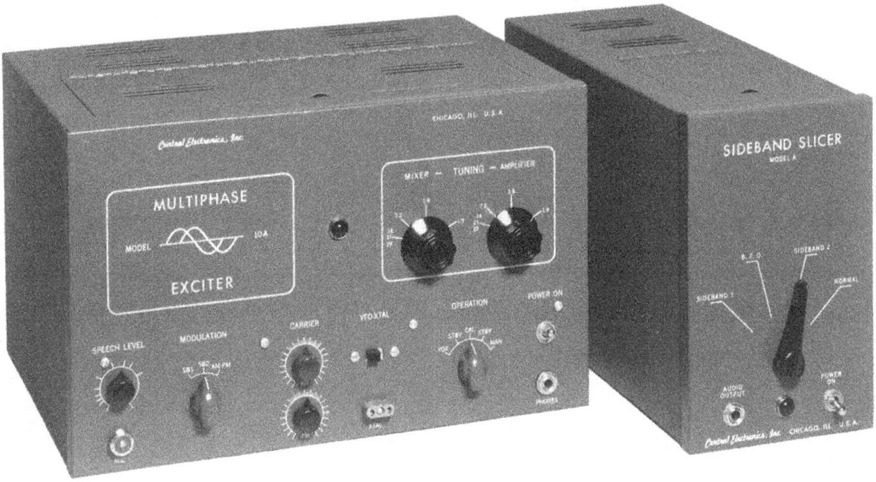

Central Electronics Model 10A and Model A Slicer

It was actually not just one product he had in mind, but *two*. The Model 10A would become the actual sideband generator/exciter unit. Yet radio communications is a two-way street; one had to receive sideband signals as well as transmitting them. Central's companion Model A Sideband Slicer would be the company's answer for converting broad-as-a-barn-door AM receivers into units capable of good sideband reception. The Model A Slicer couldn't fix a drifty receiver, but if enough receivers could stay put and not drift off-frequency long enough to not become a hinderance, then sideband for the masses would have a chance.

Helping people to get the most out of early sideband meant operator training. To Wes' way of thinking, if he could demonstrate to newcomers the operational advantages of sideband and coach them along the journey, he could warm most anyone toward the technology—and win them as customers. Little did he know that he had stumbled onto the key for Central's early success. He had also kicked a previously settled and mostly quiet AM ant hive.

The 10A encompassed the important elements a budding sidebander would need to get a proper, flexible single sideband signal on air. Using the Dome audio phase shifter, sideband suppression in the order of 40dB was possible over the important 300–3000Hz audio bandpass. The unit included voice operated transmit or VOX features and what would now be considered break-in CW. Using VOX, if a person was speaking in a start and stop fashion, the system would quickly toggle between transmit and receive modes automatically, thereby allowing a back-and-forth conversation that was untypical of AM phone operations. The 10A exciter developed 5 watts of sideband output, which was more than sufficient to drive a 1kW external final amplifier. A spotting function was included to net the exciter onto the desired receive frequency.

Unlike most homebrew exciters, the 10A could develop a fully suppressed sideband signal on any amateur band and separate plug-in coils for that purpose were available as options. A VFO could be fashioned using military surplus BC 457 or 458 model transmitters. Central even provided a matching custom case for such field modified VFO units or could supply them as wired accessory units. If a VFO was unavailable, it was possible to operate the 10A via crystals plugged into a front-panel located socket. Wes considered building his own VFO unit, and even gave it a name: V-10. Yet, when surplus 458 units could be had for $5 each, doing so made no sense.

An abbreviated schematic of the 10A, showing the sideband generating portion minus the built-in power supply and bias switching circuitry, follows.

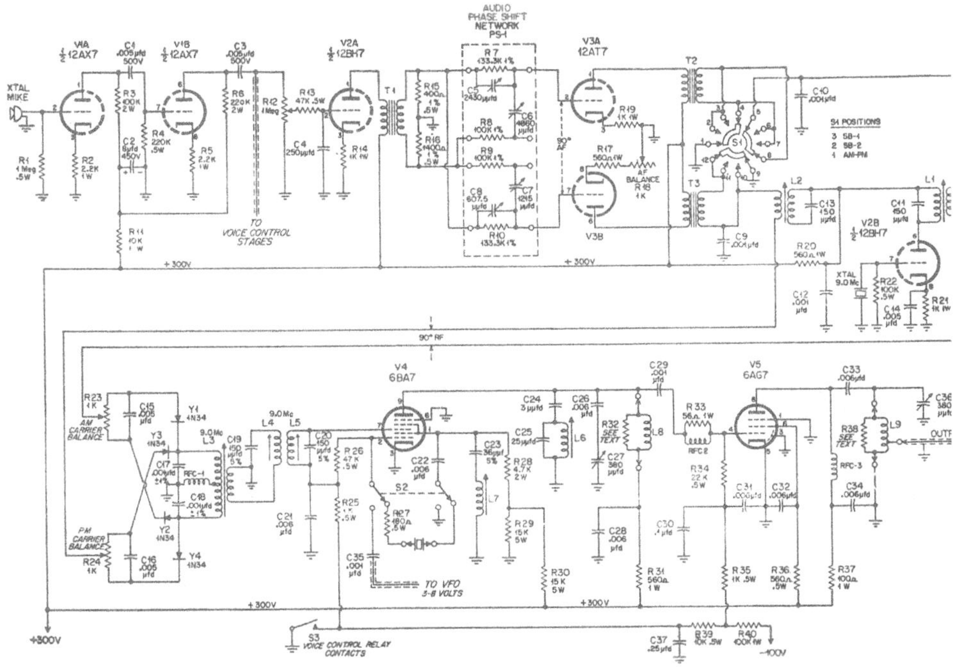

Central 10A Schematic Diagram

Incoming microphone speech energy is first amplified in two stages by a 12AX7 dual triode, V1. This then drives V2a, one half of a 12BH7 dual triode. This and transformer T1 are used to derive two separate audio channels. These two channels have audio level differences in the order of 2:7 because the insertion losses within the RC all pass network (PS-1) differ, and so must be driven per the 2:7 ratio. A 12AT7 (V3) is used to drive high to low impedance transformers, which provide an appropriate input match to the two balanced modulators. AF balance potentiometer R18 allows for equalization adjustment of the audio levels to the balanced modulator. This is necessary to compensate for transconductance variations between the two V3 triode sections and related component tolerance differences.

Function switch S1 allows the operator to select either upper or lower sideband. In addition, it is possible to unbalance the modulator and create either amplitude or phase modulated emissions. At that time, phase modulation was viewed as a means of lower-noise operation on "noisy" bands, and was included for those experimenting on 160 meters.

The balanced modulators are fed with 9MHz RF energy as developed by the crystal oscillator 12BH7 (V2b). The phase shift is due to the capacitive coupling between V2b's tank circuit L1/C11 and the secondary L2/C13. Functionally, L1 is tuned slightly above 9MHz and L2 is tuned slightly below. The coupling between the two is made adjustable by varying the separation distance (slightly via a slotted coil mounting hole) until the 90-degree phase difference is made spot-on during system alignment.

Potentiometers R23 and R24 are provided to null the undesired carrier from each of the two balanced modulators. The double sideband energy resultant from each of the two balanced modulators is combined in L3. It is here where one sideband is phase-cancelled, whereas the desired sideband is reinforced. Note that a bandpass filter, L4 and L5, is included and is necessary to suppress the 2nd harmonic of the 9MHz local oscillator. The next stage, consisting of a 6BA7 (V4) is a mixer used to heterodyne the 9MHz sideband energy to the appropriate operating frequency and band. Switch S5 permits use of an external VFO or crystal.

Since the 10A utilizes a heterodyning scheme, operation on 75 meters (and 20 meters) would require the use of an appropriate 5MHz VFO or crystal in the 5MHz range. For example, if operation was needed at 3.9MHz, the needed input signal (either VFO or crystal) must be 9MHz minus 3.9MHz, or 5.1MHz. Conversely, using the same crystal and the appropriate 20-meter plug in coil set, the exciter would produce a signal at 9MHz plus 5.1MHz, or 14.1MHz.

A 6AG7 (V5) power pentode is the exciter's final amplifier stage. The 6AG7 was selected due to its high plate dissipation (9 watts) and intended use as a high linearity video amplifier stage of television systems. Normally, in the standby mode, both the mixer and final amplifier stages are block-biased to cutoff via a -100V internal voltage source. When placed in the transmit mode, blocking bias is removed from the 6BA7 mixer and-10 volts is applied to the 6AG7 grid, which is appropriate for low-distortion linear amplifier operation.

The 10A will provide 5 watts PEP output (10 watts DC input) if appropriate VFO drive is available. The design target was for 8V RMS VFO injection. Normally, crystal operation provided somewhat higher drive levels than either the companion BC 457 or 458 VFO could typically supply. Since 10A exciters were often operated with an external power amplifier, minor power level variations were inconsequential.

Many amateurs had learned that single sideband signals could be copied on AM receivers if the internal beat frequency oscillator (BFO) had a sufficiently high injection level. While some receivers had high enough BFO level, most did not. A compromise could be met by turning the receiver's RF gain down and "riding" the AF gain/volume control. By reducing the incoming sideband signal, it would be possible to demodulate while using an also low-level BFO injection signal.

This worked to a fashion, but it wasn't great and obviously was counter-productive to holding QSOs with weak DX sidebanders[7].

Central's Model A Sideband Slicer solved the detection problem and was a major performance enhancement for receivers having low

7 Lowering the gain of the receiver's first RF amplifier in this manner served to bring a receiver's fixed BFO injection level into the proper relationship to demodulate singe sideband signals, yet this lowered the receiver's ability to detect weak incoming signals. As receiver technology improved and product detectors followed by fast-acting/slow-release automatic gain control systems became available, then the need for manually reducing RF gain in this manner was circumvented.

BFO injection. It provided an ability to selectively demodulate either sideband with the flick of a switch. In short, the Model A Slicer brought much needed performance and convenience of use improvements to many then-available receivers. A simplified Model A schematic follows:

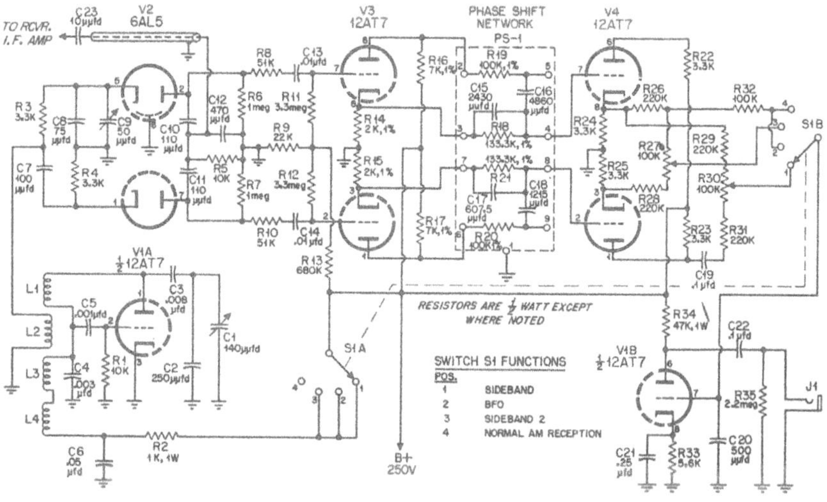

Central Model A Slicer Schematic

Electrically, the Model A Sideband Slicer is inserted between the receiver's last IF stage and first audio amplifier. It essentially replaced the receiver's normal BFO and diode demodulator stages. One half of a 12AT7 (V1a) serves as a 455kHz local oscillator which feeds a 6AL5 (V2) set of diode detectors. These two detected output signals are RF filtered and the resultant audio signals are amplified by a 12AT7 (V3), passed through a 90-degree audio phase shift network, and then are combined in the two 12AT7 (V4) triodes.

The selector switch, S1, permits detection of sideband 1, BFO (or exalted compatible AM Detection), sideband 2, and a bypass mode using the receiver's normal detection scheme.

Using the Model A slicer for AM reception brought important advantages. If for example, interference was to exist on one sideband, the opposite one could be selected, since both AM sidebands contain identical speech information, and in many cases the interference could be circumvented. In short, a 50% QRM reduction in AM detection was then possible; because the internal BFO signal of the Slicer is nearly 200 times higher than the incoming signal, detection of AM signals using the BFO plus one sideband scheme produces copy in faded conditions that is nearly free of distortion.

Wes Schum's Central Electronics had essentially leapfrogged its competitors by developing a complete transmission and reception solution for the beginning ham sidebander available in either kit or wired form.

The first Model 10A exciters were sold in mid-1951 as kits in the Chicago area and gradually expanded into Wisconsin and Michigan by word of mouth. Early manuals for those initial 10As are easy to recognize; they were each hand typed and the various sideband alignment drawings hand traced by Marge Schum! By 1952, sales were indeed brisk and growing, but that's getting ahead of the story.

The "factory" started in the Giddings Street basement but quickly expanded to the family's garage, with the car relegated to the curb. Wes and Roy Sherman (CE's first employee) built work benches, installed space heaters, and built parts shelving. Wes, Roy, and Marge kitted parts into shippable 10A/Slicer packages. At night, once the sun dropped and 75 meters came alive, Wes, Roy or

2125 Giddings Home Factory in 1950

both would be on the air…3999.5kHz, talking up their exciters. On weekends, they would visit the many hamfests in the area and local club meetings, explaining all things sideband: why it was important, what it could do, how to listen to sidebanders, and how to get active.

Their shoe-leather approach took off. More kit orders came in and with the money they produced, each sale helped Central Electronics became better organized.

The growing workload demanded more help. To keep costs low, Wes employed students from the DeVry Technical School to manage inventory, kit parts, and to ship units. The houses along West Giddings Street shared a back-service alley with the next street. The alley was lined by car garages on either side, which presented an opportunity. One by one, Wes rented garages to accommodate his increasing storage needs. One garage held transformers, another held cabinets and chassis parts, and a third held electronic components and subassemblies (primarily phase shift networks for the 10A and Slicer).

By the end of 1952, the Giddings operation was bursting at the seams. The company's first ad in the September 1952 issue of *QST* created an order avalanche. The fledgling operation had grown to include five neighbors' garages, in addition to the Schum garage and basement: five garages for parts, the Schum garage for building assembled units, and the basement for final tests and shipping. DeVry workers were often seen scrambling up and down the service alleyway pushing wheelbarrows of parts, either incoming or outgoing. Nobody at Central Electronics was complaining, but surely the neighborhood was being held hostage! Those garages were humming 12 or more hours a day during the week, and most weekends as well.

It was time to consider a move.

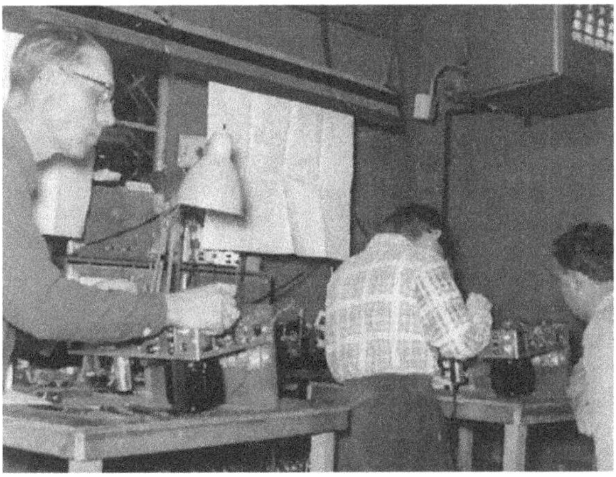

Father and son build CE 10A at Gidding Street in 1952

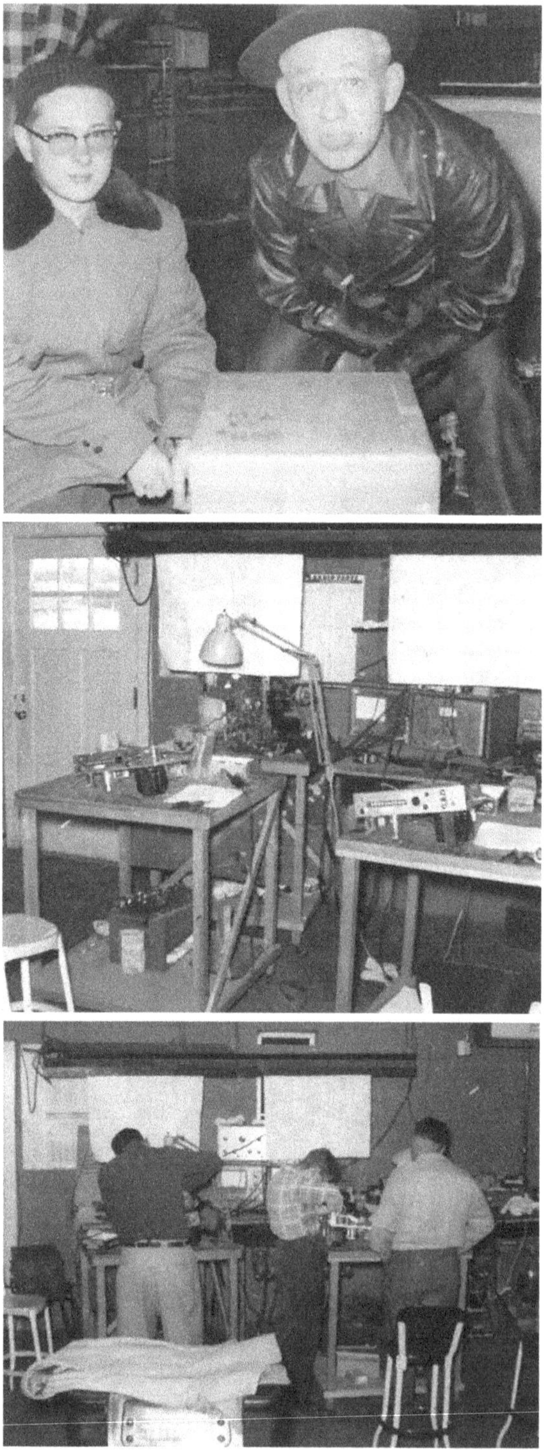

Father and son build CE 10A at Gidding Street in 1952

Former CE Factory on West Belmont Avenue

Marge was the one who spotted it: a for-lease sign outside a four-story building on West Belmont Avenue. It was an impressive brick structure, with railway access in the back: perfect for Railway Express pickups and delivery. It even included a huge all-floor service elevator that could accommodate a small forklift. She was ready and determined for Central Electronics to move from the Schum family home; it had become a major hassle for the neighbors, and to her. Marge was dog tired of making late night sandwiches for the lingering troops and daughter No. 2, Carol, had been added to the family.

The new facility on Belmont was perfect. Its location was in a hotbed of radio part suppliers and sheet metal shops. The bottom basement level was used by a machine shop, but the upper floors were available. Wes negotiated a lease for the second and third levels that included automatically renewed options. The second level, even with the railway platform, was where Central's main manufacturing, model shop, final test and shipping areas would be located. The company's business office, engineering lab, drafting department, coil department, and parts storage areas were located on the third level.

By then, Wes had added Frank Schwartz, Nick Fishik, and Tom Clemens to the operation, along with the DeVry troops. Frank and Nick were alumni from Cover Dual-Signal Systems; Tom Clemens was a young man just beginning his professional career in radio electronics. (More about them later.)

The move to the new building was not one for the faint of heart, particularly since it occurred during a Chicago winter, in December 1953, and was done by mid-January. Anyone who has visited Chicago in the winter, with the icy winds blasting off Lake Michigan, would wonder about that timing. New work benches had to be built, office furniture had to be bought (used, of course), and parts and test equipment had to be moved and organized.

Meanwhile, Wes had tried to build and kit as many 10A/Slicer units as possible to keep sales deliveries going while the move was underway. The buying ham community knew little of the move, since it wasn't promoted in any big way. The only real way of knowing a change had happened was if someone noticed the company's address listing in its January *QST* ad versus that in February. Somehow, when the dust settled, the place looked like it had always been on Belmont Street. CE was back in full swing, and Giddings Street was returned to wholesome family normalcy, much to the neighborhood's delight!

Before moving on, perhaps a story about the little 10A exciter?

The Korean War was in play and the Cold War with Russia heating up. Voice of America (VOA) had set up a broadcast station in Germany, beaming news and information (our form of propaganda) to the Russian people. The Russian government wanted this stopped, so a 500kW jamming station was built and tuned to VOA's carrier frequency. The sheer strength of that 500kW carrier obliterated VOA reception in Russia.

One day, Wes got a call from a VOA engineer-ham operator stationed in Germany who happened to have a 10A. He was wondering if Wes could suggest a way to counteract the Russian jammer. The two talked for a bit, and then Wes had an idea. He asked if the VOA transmitter was plate modulated. The engineer said no, it was essentially a 25kW linear amplifier driven by a 10-watt carrier-exciter. With its Rhombic antenna's 10dB of gain with an effective radiated power of now 250kW, Wes had a sneaky idea.

Wes said, "How about this: Use the 10A as a double-sideband/no carrier exciter. Let its signal drive your big linear amplifier. Transmit your programming in double sideband with suppressed carrier, and let the Russian jammer supply the carrier needed for demodulation by a standard AM receiver. In essence, let the jammer do the carrier's dirty work."

The VOA engineer tried it, and the idea worked. VOA's broadcast was getting through, compliments of the Russian jammer!

It took about a month, but the Russians came up with a countermeasure: They warbled the jamming carrier's frequency, which then disrupted the sideband energy thereby jammed VOA.

Another call to Wes from Germany, and yet another answer!

Wes asked if VOA had a remotely located monitoring station miles away from the transmitter site. Yes, it turned out they did; it was located nearly 30 miles away from VOA's transmitter site, and could only barely hear VOA's transmitter since the receiver site was on the back side of the Rhombic. "Perfect!" Wes said. "Now build an FM detector for your receiver, and tune to the Russian warbler. The detector will develop DC offset levels that vary in rate and direction as the Russian jammer warbles its frequency."

Wes then gave instructions to the engineer on how to change the 10A's master oscillator to one that would change frequency in step with the remote receiver's varying DC offset levels. By so doing, the 10A's signal would track the wandering jammer, and Wes had crafted possibly one of the largest HF feedback loops at the time.

It worked! The Russian jammer—sensing defeat—moved away, presumably to find someone less clever to bother. A $125 Central Electronics 10A and a Voice of America's ham engineer in Germany beat the Russians at their own game.

Chapter 11: Don't Confuse Me with the Facts

A company can never just rest on its laurels and expect sales to continue forever. CE had been cranking out 10As for well over two years. It was seen by many as a breakthrough rig and readily advanced sideband use in ham radio. It met the needs of kit builders who wanted to experiment with the new mode, as well as appliance operators who didn't care to build a rig: those who just wanted to turn it on and operate it.

As more and more of these little rigs arrived in ham homes, interesting things began happening. Initially, most were content to operate their 10As QRP-style: just 5 watts right to the antenna. Remarkably, these little rigs more than held their own against 100watt AM rigs, much to the consternation of the AM crowd. Next, came time to build some "shoes" for those barefoot rigs. If 5 watts could be so effective, what about 100 or 200 watts?

For this, experimenters tried all manner of tubes: multiple 807s or 1625s (the 12-volt version of 807s). Some made grounded grid amplifiers using as many as four 6AG7s—and abused them mightily. The tubes were rated upward of 400 volts on the plates, but that didn't stop enterprising hams from creeping a poor 6AG7's plate voltage up as high as 900V! Keep in mind, 6AG7s in 1950 were dirt cheap, so abusing a few was no big deal, if it gave a guy a whopping signal...even if it was only for one weekend! One fellow proclaimed to Wes a peak power of 300 watts, achieved using four 6AG7 with those poor tubes placed upside down, the metal envelopes sitting in a small tank of transformer oil.

Ham experimenters will truly try anything once.

Others took a more measured approach and homebrewed pairs of 6146s, a single 811A, or Eimac 4-65s into compact amplifiers. Now, here is where the real fun started. Several fellows, such as Art Collins and Leo Farber, began showing up on 20 meters with their big time KW-1 transmitters. These were king of the road rigs, but those pesky Central Electronic 10As and single 811A amplifiers or pairs of 6146s were running rings around those plate modulated kW behemoths! The sideband boys were working DX like mad men while the AMers were all carrier and no talk power.

Leo Farber

One by one they flipped. First Leo K9EH ordered his 10A/458VFO combo from Wes and asked for hints on how to convert his KW-1 to operate as a linear amplifier. Then *the* telephone call came just after Central had moved onto Belmont Avenue. It went something like this:

"Hello, Wes. This is Art Collins; do you know who I am?"

"Oh sure, Art. What can I do for you?"

"Well Wes, I've been hearing those 10A exciters of yours on the air. I was wondering if you would sell one of them to me."

"Oh, of course Art. But you see, I have a problem. We're all sold out of assembled units, and it will be several weeks before I can furnish a wired one to you. Now, if you have anyone over there that can wire kits, I can ship you one immediately."

Art hesitated for a minute, probably barely controlling his temper while weighing his next comment to this insolent upstart.

"Well, Wes, I believe we can *somehow* manage. Please send it over."

And Wes did, the same day…and then weeks went by. Neither he or his on-air friends had heard a peep out of Art, or really anyone in Cedar Rapids using a 10A. He had just about forgotten about the rig when he got another telephone call.

It was Art again.

"Wes, this is Art Collins. We have a problem: Our guys can't get your 10A to work. Can you talk them through it, please?"

"Sure, Art. Have them call me, and we'll get them going."

Minutes later, the telephone rang and a conversation about the 10A ensued. The problem was simple: Nobody at Collins had bothered to read the wiring and setup instructions. They simply wired the rigs from the schematic, plugged an in-band 14.250MHz "rock" into the front panel crystal jack, and all they got in return was a carrier: no modulation, and no carrier null. The Collins guys didn't realize, since no one bothered to read the manual, that the 10A used a heterodyne scheme; on-channel crystals wouldn't work.

Soon the 10A sold to Art Collins was heard on the air at odd hours. Art's KW-1 was likewise modified for linear operation as was Leo Farber's. So, those two KW-1s did AM, CW, sideband, and phase modulation; with their high-powered power amplifiers, they were now kings of the sideband road. Those two were not the only KW-1s to get the sideband treatment. And bigger homebrewed amplifiers using massive Eimac 4-1000 tubes began popping up as California-sized kilowatts.

A month later, Wes got another call from Cedar Rapids. Art was on the line once again.

"Hi, Wes. We'd like to buy three more of those 10As—but this time, no kits!"

They both got a big laugh out of that before hanging up, and would remain friendly competitors for years. It was quite some time later that Wes discovered those last three 10As had made their way to Collins' sideband development lab and were used as signal sources, as part of Collins' ongoing development of new receivers and transmitters for the amateur market. But the story doesn't end here. Years later, at the wedding reception of one of his grandsons, Wes found himself seated at a table with the bride's grandparents when all of a sudden, he heard the words "Collins! Central!" ring out. It turned out that the grandfather of the bride had been an engineer for Collins. They had a wonderful time celebrating the marriage of their grandchildren and reminiscing about the good old days of electronics.

But what happens when the well runs dry? Eventually, everyone who wanted a 10A would have one—and worse, competitors were springing up and entering the market. Wes was already looking to the next step: a reason why hams should buy an exciter to replace their 10As. His new rig had to have new features and wider flexibility than the 10A.

That new rig became the Model 20A.

Model 20A

Model 20A chassis

The 20A was housed in the same cabinet as the 10A, but with important new features. The plug-in coils had been ditched, replaced by a fully bandswitched internal mixer and PA tuned circuits, which allowed operation on 160 meters through 10 meters. A new carrier insertion control was added that allowed an operator to supply carrier for tuning a linear amplifier but without having to rebalance the carrier null controls. A second 6AG7 was added to provide more drive for the largest 1kW external amplifiers. A 6E5 eye tube was added as a carrier null/relative power indicator to simplify carrier balance and mixer/power amplifier tuning.

A couple of the DeVry helpers were stunned. One young man questioned Wes. "We're running flat-out now! Why are you designing a new rig? We're selling all of the 10As we can make!" Wes replied, "Don't confuse me with the facts! I know what I'm doing. People hate having to open the 10A and deal with coils just to change bands. We'll sell far more 20As."

And they did indeed. Nearly 7,500 Model 20A rigs were sold between mid-1954 through 1959. By comparison, slightly more than 2,500 Model 10As and 1,500 Model 10B (improved 10A) units were sold.

Revamped 10A became the 10B

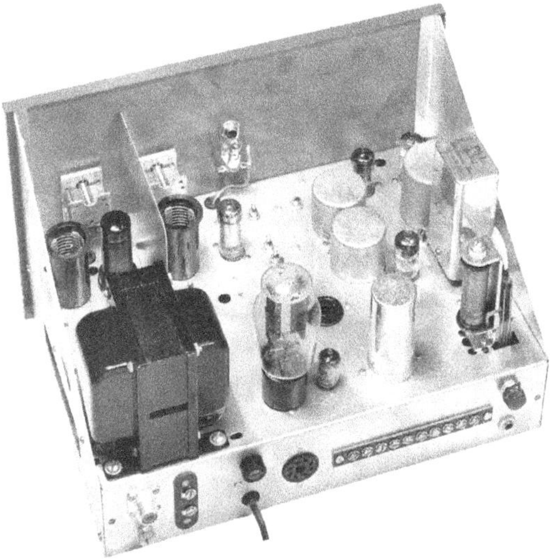

10B chassis

Central Electronics had in relatively short order become an amateur radio sideband powerhouse. It then owned the amateur single sideband market, in terms of on-air exciters. While unit sales of 20As were sky-rocketing, Wes and his engineering team were keen on developing a new scheme that would open eyes wide. They were in a race to develop the most advanced radio transmitter of its kind.

It would be called the 100V.

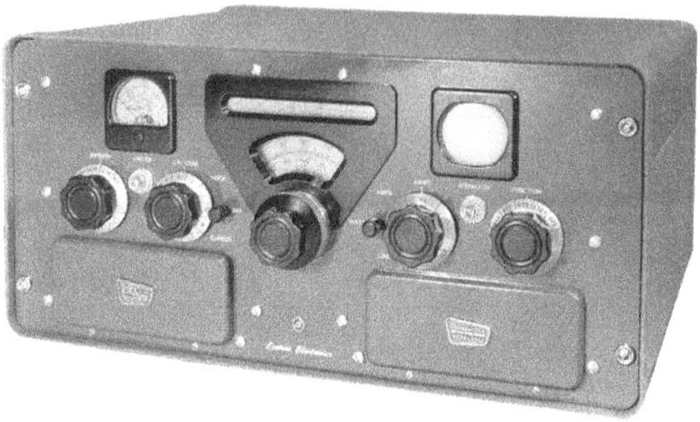

Model 100V

The seeds for the 100V transmitter and 600L linear amplifier started with a chance meeting between Wes Schum and Joe Batchelor at a hamfest in 1952. Joe had come to Chicago allegedly to enter his mobile rig in a homebrew contest, but his real mission was to meet Wes Schum.

Joe lived in Walnut Grove, Georgia, a small town outside of Atlanta. He was born in in 1922 and like Wes (and many others) became interested in electronics at a young age. While he lived in small-town USA, Joe's understanding of mathematics and electronics grew exponentially through his teen years. You see, Joe Batchelor, W4EGK, was an off-the-charts genius, a guy with an enormous IQ and an inane instinct for radio electronics. Although he graduated from college after the war, Joe was more than anything self-taught; he soon found himself thinking far beyond his college professors.

If it had anything to do with radio or television, Joe was your man. In 1949, he and his wife Jackie opened Joe's Radio Service in Walnut Grove, Georgia. Back then, televisions were available as kits and Joe's would build TVs on order for local area customers, along with servicing the community's factory-made TVs and radio units.

That was during the day; at night, Batchelor found himself drawn to single sideband and the Stanford experiments like a moth drawn to a lightbulb on a hot summer's night. He couldn't learn enough about sideband through the published literature, so Joe embarked on his own experiments, building several phasing-type sideband exciters of his own design...some of which he sold to local area hams.

Several things bugged Joe about the published designs available. For one, the balanced modulators people had been constructing were frequency limited. Joe felt the answer for a broad-banded balanced modulator could be solved using a bifilar-wound transformer. He felt this would be inherently wide band and would allow the modulator to function over a wide carrier frequency range without tuned circuits. That, he ultimately perfected.

Now, Joe did not enjoy a war deferment as Wes had. He had joined the Army Air Corps during the war and was intrigued by the Collins ART-13 autotune transmitter. That unique transmitter could be pre-tuned for operation on multiple channels. Within a minute, a channel change could be had, after a mesmerizing, pre-programmed set of motor-operated adjustments had been concluded. Joe was fascinated by its operation, but thought if this could be done electronically, without cams or motors, then that would be the ultimate in multichannel transmitter operation.

That, more than anything, stuck in Joe's mind. Making that tuning happen near-instantly would open many commercial avenues. Transmitters could be operated unattended, and frequency usage could be agile. Flick a switch, and in a second—not several minutes—operation could be available on multiple frequencies. No more dipping the plate and increasing the load. He couldn't stop thinking about it.

First, he thought about the tuning process. That involved matching a high impedance plate load—on the order of 1,500 to several thousand ohms—to a low impedance antenna. Wouldn't a parallel-tuned tank, coupled to a series-tuned L network, do it? Yes...but how to accomplish the coupling, and how to make it automatic?

To not kill himself, Joe's first set of experiments revolved around the relatively low plate voltage, low-cost/ham-friendly 807 tube. He then made a traditional plate tuned circuit for the 807, operable at 4MHz. Taping off a portion of the tank coil near the mid-point, he used a series capacitor and a variable inductor to form a series L network. After many long nights, Joe eventually got a network that provided a viable power transfer to a 50-ohm load.

Great…now he had to figure out how to get rid of the tuning adjustments. Maybe if instead of using a variable coupling capacitor, a bifilar wound coil having the right amount of turn-to-turn capacitive coupling could be conjured up. After some insulation fits and starts, and lots of cut and try, he got a decent result: a bifilar-stray capacitance that could series tune the high side of the L network. What about the parallel network's capacitor? OK, the tube has plate capacitance that is set by the geometry of the tube's internal elements, plus there is stray capacitance involved with the output stage's wiring and physical parts placement. Could Joe use that "free" stray capacity to make a parallel tank? Yes, but due to the low-capacity values involved, more coil inductance was needed—and it subsequently had downstream impact on the L network's prior work.

It seemed if you changed one thing, it impacted other aspects of the network. This cut-and-try, squeeze-the-balloon approach went on throughout late 1949 and into 1951. One thing Joe Batchelor never did is give up, particularly if he believed a solution was viable and that the "damned thing had to work."

What was remarkable was Joe didn't have a sweep generator/oscilloscope package (now termed a network analyzer) to visually understand the passband response and efficiency of his design. With each iteration, he, with his wife Jackie's help, would measure the network's input versus output frequency response and plot those on graph paper, point by point.

The monks copying Bibles by hand had nothing on them. The Batchelors had signed up for tedious, slow work. Only Joe's dogged determination kept them at the job, night after night.

Eureka; success! One winter night Joe got what he was looking for. He had cut and tried his way to a network that covered the 80M band, from 3.5MHz to 4.5MHz, having an essentially flat bandpass that matched the 807's plate load impedance and delivered power (within1dB) to a 50-ohm load across that full 1MHz band. The winning network was finally at hand, using a plastic baby bottle as its coil form!

Along with the mobile rig, Joe's baby bottle coupler went to Chicago and met its soon-to-be-uncle, Wes Schum. Next, Joe would need to scale couplers for operation on other amateur bands and mate the concept with a hefty transmitting tube. Why not an 813?

Joe Batchelor's baby bottle coupler

Chapter 12: Batchelor Joins CE

No doubt Wes was conflicted by this unknown fellow who had sought him out. Sure, he had brought along a neat little mobile rig to enter the Chicago hamfesters homebrew contest, but why travel all that distance to show off a mobile rig? That's a really long car ride in the summer and with no air conditioning. Surely, similar events must have gone on in the Southeast.

Hmmm.

He and Joe had QSOed before, but the conversations were typical: signal reports, discussions about audio quality and sideband phase shift networks. Nothing that would hint about what Joe had in mind. When the two finally met, over hot dogs and Cokes, it came out loud and clear: Joe had some unusual, potentially patentable ideas and was wanting to know if Central Electronics was interested. Wes listened, but was put off at first. In person, this Batchelor fellow was an imposing figure, tall and red haired, with a Van Dyke beard and smoking a cigar. He was loud, animated—and from a sound and accent standpoint, bore a strong resemblance to the rooster cartoon character Foghorn Leghorn.

As Joe kept talking and described his recent work, Wes' interest perked up. He soon forgot all about those physical aspects and zeroed in on the message. Joe's bifilar balanced modulator concept was nice, but that no-tune impedance matching coupler made skyrockets fly in

Wes' mind. This could be a truly revolutionary idea that went far beyond amateur radio. Wes was sure the military would *love* this.

The hamfest for those two ended at lunch, as they later reconvened at Giddings Street to discuss how some of Joe's ideas could factor into the CE product portfolio. If a deal could be struck, both men stood to profit handsomely. A no-tune sideband transmitter—a product that was self-contained, instantly bandswitched, and had, say, 100 watts of output—would be an instant success. Joe, living in rural Georgia, knew he lacked the supportive infrastructure of machinists, model makers, metal fab shops, assemblers, and parts suppliers to build a commercial product on his own. He needed Wes far more than maybe either recognized at the time.

The two parted but agreed to continue to talk about a potential association and how that might be structured. With Joe headed back toward Georgia and Chicago in his rearview mirror, Wes huddled up with Jay Warren, Marge and his father, Leo, to talk it through, hoping to see if some sort of association or even a partnership made sense. Warren, after hearing about these new ideas, was interested but skeptical. "Let's see if Joe can build couplers for other amateur bands. Maybe his 75 meter work was just a fluke. Before offering any sort of deal, let's get more information and real proof that to see if this broadband concept is not only possible, but reproducible."

Later that week, a telephone call was placed, and Joe accepted the challenge: make a new Bachelor-style output network coupler for 20 meters.

Working alone, just he and his wife Jackie, they did just that—although it took several months of late nights to yield a viable result. Joe sent test data to Central Electronics for them to chew on. Not seeing anything wrong with the plotted frequency response results, and after hearing the new coupler in action on 20 meters, the next part of the challenge had to be met: build a coupler at the Giddings Street operation in Chicago.

Joe and Jackie Batchelor in 1995

This was a new challenge for Joe and Jackie. Joe's Radio Service was their haven. It was set up to build and experiment but was clearly not easily movable. They had built special test equipment to measure input and output impedance. It was 'special' because the two lacked money to buy anything commercially made, so Joe figured out how to build his own. It worked, but in typical Joe fashion it was a lashed together mess with no thought given to transportability. A cleaned-up version was clearly needed, and subsequently constructed.

Physically winding the hundreds of test couplers the two had made before hitting paydirt was a painfully slow process. Eventually, they fashioned a more viable winding jig built by using parts from an ancient sewing machine and bits found in a town scrap yard. It was too cumbersome to travel, so a new winder unit had to be devised. All of this took time; Wes and Jay Warren began to believe that this coupler thing was a mirage.

Out of the blue one Friday afternoon, Joe called and said he was ready to build couplers if Wes and Company were still interested.

"Of course, come on up!" Wes exclaimed.

Days later, Joe and Jackie were relaxing in the Schum living room and planning out how to commence coil winding the next morning. With Wes, Warren, and Roy Sherman as onlookers, the pair assembled their equipment, started to describe the design and winding process, and then went to work. Over the next several days, 75 meter and 20 meter couplers were wound, installed, and then tested in Joe's little 807 test chassis.

They weren't shining examples of quality workmanship, but electrically they worked, and the results were clearly reproducible. The test results on those newly wound couplers closely mirrored what the pair had logged in Georgia. Best of all, Joe admitted that he had gone a bit further in his at-home design work. By then he was running a 4-125 tetrode on 75 meters—broadbanded and no-tuning, of course!

Now, it was time for Central Electronics and the Batchelors to talk turkey.

The group eventually came to an agreement in principle: A new company, Patronix, would be formed as a holding company for patents filed and awarded to Wes or Joe. Central Electronics would pay for the preparation of such patents. Joe would become a salaried employee, would receive a minority distribution of company stock (20%) if certain production objectives were met, and earn a 3% royalty on every item sold that contained circuitry based on Batchelor's patented work.

After minor agreement changes and final review by the attorneys, a deal was struck. Joe's first assignment was to complete work involving the bifilar balanced modulator and get it into the patent pending process. This device utilized a specially constructed transformer having two bifilar-wound primary windings and a tightly coupled low impedance secondary. The bifilar transformer configuration allowed for the modulator to maintain balance over the range of 1.5MHz to 30MHz, if constructed according to the patent-disclosed design.

A patent application for the bifilar balanced modulator was subsequently filed on July 30th, 1953 and eventually granted: US Patent

2,856,587 on October 14th, 1958. The likely reasons for the grant's delay were the application's six broadly structured claims, challenged by the Patent Office's examiners.

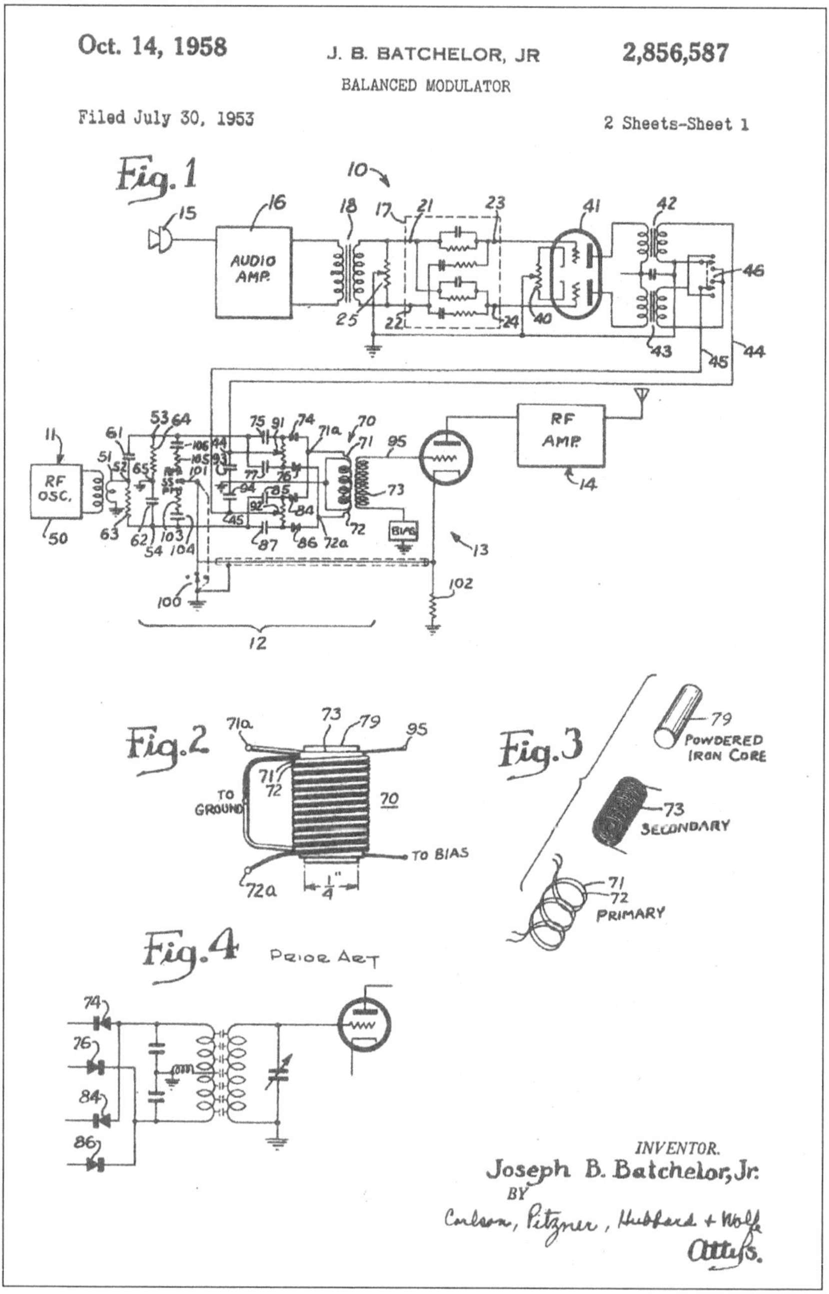

US Patent 2,856,587 Batchelor Balanced Modulator

The Batchelor balanced modulator potentially could have been added to the Model 10A or subsequent Model 20A exciter designs, but since those units operate at a fixed 9MHz and the current configuration was proven to work, such a change was deemed unnecessary. The patented Batchelor design found a home in future Central Electronics products, a version of which became the basis of the Bifilar RF Level Compressor used in the Model 100R receiver prototype, developed by the Zenith Radio Corporation's military operation.

The true hallmark of Joe Batchelor's work at Central Electronics and what Wes viewed as hitting paydirt is described by US Patent 2,864,060 for their Electrical Coupling Device. This was the invention that would cement Central Electronics as the first to manufacture a broadband, no-tune HF ham radio transmitter, one that was fully automatic in operation. Other patents would follow, some of which became incorporated into eventual Central Electronics products while others, like their remote-tuned mobile HF antenna, failed to materialize in commercial form.

The Batchelor Broadband Coupler was the Company's crown jewel.

Initially, Joe remained in Walnut Grove, Georgia and continued his Joe's Radio Service while refining circuit ideas for Wes and Central Electronics. That remote work configuration changed though, in 1955. Difficulty in producing consistent Batchelor broadband couplers for the company's new desktop linear amplifier prompted the Batchelors to pull up stakes and relocate to Chicago. There, the young family eventually settled in suburban Libertyville and traded in their southern ways for the big city.

Central Electronics was off to the races!

Chapter 13: The 600L Amplifier and Patent 2,864,060

It was 1954: a new year, and a fresh start. Daughter No. 3, Diane, joined the ranks. The Company had just moved into more spacious facilities on West Belmont Avenue. The new Model 20A was being readied for release, and attention given to a companion amplifier for the little 10 and 20-watt pep exciters. Of course, many hams continued to homebrew equipment, with amplifiers high on the list; the ratio of kit versus assembled sideband rigs was moving steadily toward the already-built ledger, however. Wes figured that Central should build a companion amplifier and tap into that already-built market segment.

What to build? How much power should it deliver? What about its styling and features?

The styling part was easy; it needed to look like a CE radio! That meant a wrinkle-finished cabinet, smooth gray front panel, white lettering, and symmetrical layout of controls. If contained in the same sized cabinet as the exciters, then the power level could not be much beyond 300 watts and still have room for a viable plate/screen power supply.

Joe's broadband coupler concept had not yet been resolved into a patent application, so initially, the amplifier they planned to build would be a typical, manually tuned one. It would be bandswitched, though, and not use a roller inductor; those are somewhat slow to tune. They chose a single-tube 813 beam power tetrode, which could be cooled using a small fan. One 813 operated with relatively-low plate voltage and could develop 300 watts DC input, a significant power gain for the CE exciters. Plus, the 813 was available everywhere for around six bucks.

To digress for a moment, prior to the proliferation of single sideband in the late 1950s and mid-1960s, radio communications involved principally CW or AM operation; power levels were regulated by the FCC in terms of DC input power and were manually calculated as the product of panel meter indicated final amplifier plate current multiplied by DC supply plate voltage. Operators of those two modes of transmission could readily calculate their transmitter's DC input power using simple math and confirm compliance with FCC regulations.

A transmitter's actual single sideband energy is not a constant as for AM or CW transmissions but follows that of the input speech envelope. Thus, a DC input power calculation is not as readily made, since plate current values indicated on a meter would be varying and not indicative of a steady state. An assumption was subsequently made by the FCC that transmitter input power for single sideband voice would be approximately twice that of a calculated steady-state DC input level, although the DC power calculation was the one required for compliance. How's that for added confusion?! It is for this reason that commercial manufacturers would later cite transmitter input power as, for example, 1kW on CW/AM and 2kW PEP for single sideband voice.

Later, in 1982, the use of a calculated DC input power level was abandoned by the FCC and replaced by its 1,500W PEP output level limitation. The reason for the change was, allegedly, one of safety. An FCC examiner could more safely assess a transmitter's compliance with output power limits by using calibrated power (wattmeter) measuring apparatus. This action would eliminate the need for personnel to access dangerous high voltages within a transmitter's internal circuitry.

Back to Central's broadband amplifier. Work progressed with the desktop amplifier, but soon doubts came into mind that a modest 300-watt DC input would not satisfy many potential buyers. The advantages of a desktop no-tune design would be offset by the perceived lower level of performance. Worse, it was becoming a packaging challenge, stuffing all that hardware into a box as small as a CE exciter. Already the prototype's cabinet had to be stretched in width, but even that was cutting things close.

This whole exercise occupied the majority of 1954, but by November the broadband coupler was a settled down reality and the design's patent application was under development. It was safe to change direction and dump the traditional plate/load controls for just a band-switched coupler configuration. And, to sweeten the pot, Wes wanted to add new features to make the desktop unit irresistibly reliable and fun to operate.

First, the power level needed to be jacked up to 600 watts. That meant higher plate voltage. It was also well understood that excellent dynamic voltage regulation was an essential ingredient for low-distortion sideband signals and Wes was determined that that Central's amplifier would meet that objective. The 600L, as it was now called, would have a choke input filter followed by a 45uF oil-filled mylar filter capacitor. Mylar capacitors having high capacity and voltage ratings were then being used on photoflash systems. Wes tracked down a supplier, determined a capacitor of that type would last for ages, and factored it into the new design.

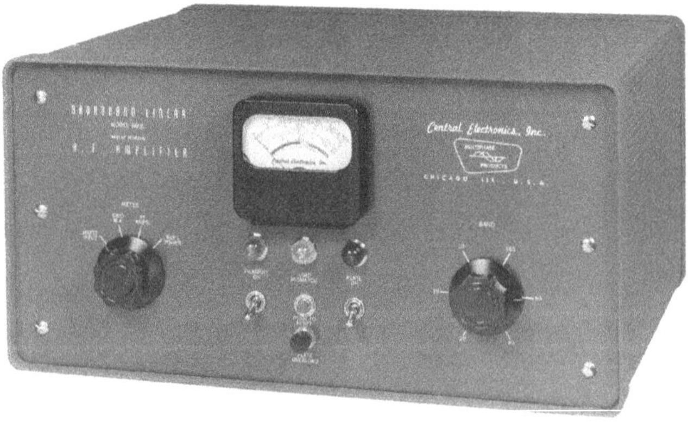

600L Broadband Amplifier

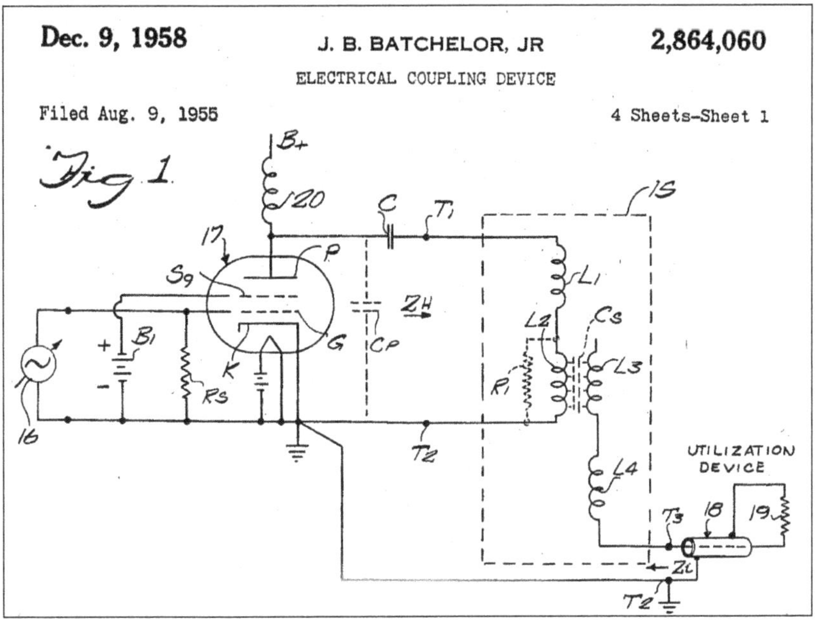

US Patent 2,864,060

Figuring the 816 mercury vapor rectifiers should be surge-protected, he then added what might be the first step-start circuit installed in a commercially made amateur amplifier power supply. A 10-ohm/50-watt resistor, shunted by normally open relay contacts, was included in the plate transformer's primary circuit wiring. When the amplifier's plate switch was first activated, the series resistor served to limit the transformer's inrush current for approximately one second, after which the normally open contacts across the resistor would close and full power would then be applied to the plate transformer's primary winding. Next, Wes added a regulated screen voltage system designed by Tom Clemens W9OKA: a plate overload relay, a screen voltage protection scheme, and a metering system that directly indicated DC input power and also grid current, reflecting power and RF antenna current.

During this time, Joe was in Monroe, Georgia optimizing 160 meter to 10 meter input and output couplers for the 813 final. Each coupler pair was designed for a 1MHz bandpass and flat to within 1dB. The combination of matched input/output bandpass couplers resulted in steep out-of-band signal rejection. There was only one problem: when the Batchelor couplers were installed by Tom Clemens into constructed amplifiers, they didn't work. The couplers worked and tested fine in Georgia when installed in Joe's 813 test fixture. But in Chicago, when installed into actual production amplifiers, their bandpass was titled badly and unacceptable.

What was wrong? Tom, Wes, and Joe pulled hair out, but then the lightbulb lit: What about mutual coupling *across* couplers? The solution was to add a shorting section to the band switch that would selectively short-circuit the high impedance end of the adjacent coupler.

This was better, but not a home run.

The plate coupler's bandpass was being shifted up or down in frequency, which turned out to be caused by the RF plate feed choke. Worse, and adding to the confusion, the couplers that Tom and the coil shop personnel were winding had a 50% failure rate. Barrels were being filled with mis-tuned/mis-assembled couplers. This was beginning to feel like death by a thousand cuts. While this sort of problem is routine when pursuing new ideas along uncharted paths, it was beginning to get old. Improved winding fixtures eventually solved the coupler assembly woes. The RF choke problem was far thornier to resolve. Here, the effective capacity of the RF choke varied band to band, which subsequently detuned the couplers. The solution was not as forgiving. The design of a new RF choke—one with a capacity variance of less than 2pf band to band—fell to Joe and, as he put it, the RF choke was almost as difficult to design as the coupler!

This is when Wes dropped the hammer and directed Joe to pack up the family, his furniture, his equipment and move to Chicago *immediately*! The move took place shortly thereafter and Joe, his wife Jackie, and their three boys temporarily moved into the Schum home. Life was very interesting with seven kids under one roof, but Jackie's famous Southern biscuits helped to soothe the chaos—at least during dinner.

Finally, and with everyone working under one roof and rigid construction processes set, 600Ls began to leave the factory, if slowly a first. Getting the RF Choke design finalized had cost months, and likely resulted in lost sales. But once those no-tune amplifiers were being delivered, the delay would be forgotten. The 600L was on the cusp of earning a cult following, but after a brief initial advertising start it stopped again for an altogether different reason: a cosmetic change. The cabinetry for the new 600L was changed to match a planned new and revolutionary desktop transmitter, the 100V.

Chapter 14: The Incomparable 100V

The addition of Joe Batchelor to the Central Electronics team pushed the product idea gas pedal to the floor. Although Joe Batchelor remained in Georgia until just prior to the 600L release in late 1955, much else was happening in the background. The two were in discussion about developing a ground-breaking multi-mode transmitter that would expand well beyond the broadband coupler concept. Both men were aiming high, the energy from one spurring on the other. The one objective they seized was that this had to be a groundbreaking design if Central Electronics was to break through the accessory radio market.

While sideband exciters in the 10B (an improved Model 10A) and 20A class were flying out of Central's front doors, these were considered accessories when compared to equipment made by companies such as Collins, Hallicrafters, and EF Johnson. Collins and Hallicrafters had catapulted from the amateur market into the more lucrative military and commercial radio supplier field, their reputations well cemented by wartime-tested performance, highest quality, and renowned reliability in extreme conditions. Central Electronics was born too late to build a reputation in the way of Collins and Hallicrafters. For them, it would have to come by way of leapfrogging beyond then-current technology.

Central Electronics had to be a pioneering innovator ready to accept risks that larger companies might steer clear of, avoiding explanations to investors. It was with that mindset the two went to work. As soon as the new 20A exciter had progressed from prototype and into final production, by 1954 the general theme for their new transmitter had been minted. It would be called 100V: 100 for 100 watts of output on all bands via the Batchelor broadband coupler scheme, and V for having a self-contained VFO. From there, the real dreaming started.

Many sideband signals then heard on air suffered from all sorts of maladies: poor carrier balance, inadequate sideband suppression, and broad bandwidth, to name a few. While the Dome wideband audio phase shift network could achieve 40dB of unwanted sideband suppression, one would never guess it was based on the "quality" of some on-air signals. Even where some might get their rigs aligned to 35dB or 40dB suppression, it wouldn't last due to component value drift. Overdriving linear amplifiers to the point of saturation—which some did, regularly—would then lead to excessively broad signals, and only added fuel to those who believed single sideband to be the Satan of ham radio!

Central's new transmitter must fix all of what was wrong with then-sideband. Their rig must attain an even higher measure of sideband suppression: 50dB would be a good target. Many hams lacked test equipment to assure the purity of their sideband signals. Shouldn't the new rig have a built-in oscilloscope? That feature would give the owner/operator an ability to instantaneously observe the transmitter's linearity and prevent "flat-topping." While we're at it, why not a built-in carrier balance meter so an operator could occasionally check and confirm his rig's suppressed carrier wasn't gradually creeping up in level? And so, the list grew and the performance and feature vision for their 100V transmitter took shape.

Joe and machinist Nick Fishik tackled the VFO design while Wes and Tom Clemens thought about what driver/final amplifier tube combination to use. The VFO project took Joe and Nick down several paths. By then, Collins had perfected the permeability tuned VFO. The Collins design was rugged, and its tuning could be linearized using a combination of a variable-pitch main oscillator coil and a series-connected, small-value corrector coil whose inductance could be mechanically altered.

The alteration, while tuning across the VFO's operating range, would add or subtract a small amount of inductance as the VFO traversed from its low end to high end range of tuning, thereby correcting non-linearity.

The only shortcoming inherent in the Collins design was with the corrector coil's tracking system. By design, the track the corrector followed was preset during the VFO's manufacturing process. Once set, while the VFO's end points could be externally adjusted in the field, the track's compensation between endpoints could not since it was established by the mechanics within the VFO. Fishik thought he had an idea for making the tracking compensation changeable in the field and without having to disassemble the VFO or send it back to Central for recalibration. Off he went, perfecting his mechanical approach.

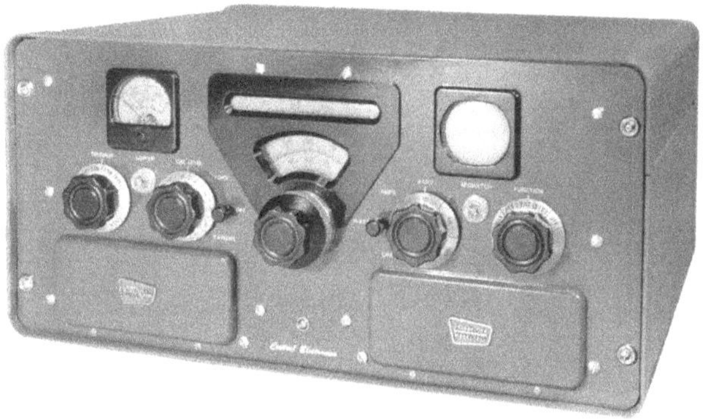

100V Transmitter

100V Transmitter interior view

Joe looked closely at the electrical aspects of a VFO design. During shop experiments, he charted the effects of plate and screen voltage variations on several designs. In time, his working design grew to include both plate and screen voltage regulation. Plate voltage regulation was straightforward using a 0A2 gas tube. Neon bulbs, while principally used as power indicators, likewise have a voltage-regulating characteristic. For NE2 bulbs, that characteristic is around 90 volts. Although the regulating voltage of a typical NE2 is in no way as precisely characterized as a true voltage regulator tube (or Zener diode, which was not around at the time), the precise voltage via the NE2 regulator was not critical. What mattered was just that once fired and operational the voltage developed across the NE2 was steady, even though the general transmitter's power supply might encounter voltage fluctuations.

Now, Joe had given his VFO a fighting chance. Both plate and screen voltages were stabilized, which would go a long way toward the stability needed for single sideband operations, but what about the filament? Collins Radio had employed Amperite ballast tubes to regulate the VFO filament voltage in its R390 and R389 receiver designs; would Batchelor's VFO need this as well? Even in the rural Georgia environs of Joe's Radio Service the measured AC line voltage was constant. Its voltage variations, if any, were small in level and slow in transition. Joe's educated guess concluded that a VFO ballast tube was an unnecessary frill for an amateur transmitter that likely would be operated for relatively short periods: hours daily, not continuously for weeks or months.

Now, how to deal with thermal frequency drift?

This turned into a battle of thermal time constant wits, and Nick Fishik came up with the answer. An oscillator's frequency may gradually drift due to minute temperature changes within the physical structure of frequency determining elements, such as the coil/capacitor resonant circuit. In most cases, the principal contributor to frequency drift is the inductor. Its change in characteristic is often one having a positive coefficient versus temperature, meaning the coil's inductance increases with temperature and that decreases the oscillator's frequency. This change can be caused by the small amount of power flowing through the coil's conductor, but is mostly due to outside heat sources. Obviously, vacuum tubes would be a significant heat-rise source and would adversely affect an oscillator's frequency stability, if not appropriately compensated for in some manner.

The normal course, and one that was used by Joe, was to add small temperature compensating capacitors that had a negative capacitance value drift versus temperature coefficient. If a viable combination of both positive and negative temperature compensation could be found, in theory, a no-drift oscillator would result.

Before attempting to neutralize drift electronically, the permeability tuned oscillator coil needs mechanical attention. Nick found that if the oscillator's inductor was wound under high tension onto a ceramic coil form and then coated with an epoxy cement, the windings could be made highly rigid and would resist mechanical deformation from heat. By so doing, smaller values of opposite-acting temperature compensation capacitors would be necessary.

Then, Joe designed an oscillator-buffer circuit that could use a low-Q VFO LC network. A low-Q network would inherently have low circulating RF current, and less propensity to frequency drift. His eventual design had one other unique characteristic: the Batchelor design was self-balancing and would maintain good VFO output as the tubes aged and transconductance decreased.

The combination of Fishik's rigid inductor assembly and Joe's oscillator having exceptionally low circulating current yielded a unit with good stability that needed only two to four 1pf frequency compensation capacitors to reduce drift to less that 20Hz per hour, after warming up. Fishik figured even better stability could be had if the group of temperature compensating capacitors could be isolated from the VFO's aluminum housing by some sort of thermal blocking arrangement. That solution was a simple one: Nick added a ceramic insulator to isolate the capacitor group. The VFO would then settle down to less than a 10Hz per hour drift after a 30-minute warmup, as good as most open-air crystal oscillators.

Batchelor and Fishik had developed a fantastic VFO. It was rugged, permeability-tuned, highly stable, free of microphonics and distortion, and had excellent end-to-end tracking over its full 1MHz range.

The 100V would have a stout VFO heart. Now for the power amplifier stage.

Wes and Tom Clemens had been testing many different tubes for driver and power amplifier use while developing the 20A. They had built test fixtures for tubes such as the 6CL6, 5763, 2E26, 6BQ6, 6CU6, 6146, etc. So, they had a good head start before design work on the 100V commenced. RCA's 6146 was a good, reliable power tube. A pair would do well in the 100-watt output class, but with respect to single sideband, the tube's linearity was poor, absent the application of RF feedback[8]. RF feedback added alignment stability and drive power concerns, but was an accepted way to deal with inherent non-linearity. So, they evaluated other tubes such as the Eimac 4-65 and even the 4X150. Those required higher plate voltage (increased cost), and in the case of the 4X150, a pressurized air source. None eliminated the need for RF feedback.

The search continued.

Wes, of course, closely followed the development of low distortion audio amplifier tubes as essential design elements for future Jay L. Warren products. Tung Sol, a well-known tube manufacturer, had introduced a new audio power tube, the 6550, that had excellent distortion specs. Amperex, known for its high-performance tubes, had also released an improved low power audio tube, the 6BQ5, as a successive enhancement to the ubiquitous 6AQ5.

Although the Tung Sol 6550 had its plate connection at the base rather than protruding from the tube envelope's top, Wes learned the tube base was mica filled. Mica, as an element, has excellent RF characteristics, and seemed to be overkill for use in an audio tube. Wes and Tom both wondered if this new tube, with its ample plate dissipation rating and excellent linearity, would work at 30MHz. They soon discovered it

8 Better linearity could also be achieved if the tubes were biased toward Class A operation, but with a reduction in output level efficiency.

would, and in fact was viable well above 50MHz. OK, what about *side-band* linearity? They conducted two-tone intermodulation distortion tests using a 6BQ5 driver/6550 amplifier combo and found the tube lineup had better than -35dB characteristics—without any feedback.

Wow! Even better linearity was achieved using the 6973, an improved high-performance 6BQ5. Test measurements found distortion products were down -40dB. The two had stumbled onto something. These highly linear audio tubes of highest quality would be outstanding candidates for their incomparable 100V.

And so it went: More feature ideas came to bear. Why not some speech processing for improved intelligibility during rough band conditions? AMers had used speech clippers and LC audio filters to increase their equipment's talk power. What about the same for sideband?

Initial hard-clipper testing produced less than desirable results, with too much in-band distortion. By integrating post-clipping feedback into their speech processing scheme, Batchelor was able to round the normally flat-topped, clipped result and thereby reduced the level of in-band distortion products. A bandpass filter would be necessary to restrict the transmitted energy and eliminate splatter. The 100V needed a filter that was compact, and like the rest of its design, new.

So, they developed a compact, single-tube active audio bandpass filter. The Batchelor design was one using bridged-T elements composed of only resistors and capacitors. The net result was a filter whose characteristics were outstanding with respect to physical size and electrical performance. Joe's filter had a flat bandpass characteristic between 200Hz and 3,500Hz but was down -40dB at 100Hz and 4kHz. It was not much larger than a pack of cigarettes—far smaller and less costly to produce than any comparable passive design.

Now that their transmitter would have speech processing, what about operating modes? Here was the huge advantage Central's phasing approach to sideband offered over a filter scheme: Phasing could easily do them all.

- Upper sideband, suppressed carrier
- Lower sideband, suppressed carrier
- Upper sideband, with carrier
- Lower sideband, with carrier
- Double sideband, suppressed carrier
- Amplitude modulation
- Phase modulation
- Continuous wave
- Frequency shift keying

Now, Central's design team had to deal with the final challenge: the sideband generator and its important audio phase shifter. For this, they sought the advice of experts: General Electric, RCA, and Stanford University. The good thing about being on the front line of a technology's development is that you are in position to develop friendships with like-minded experimenters. All wanted to see single sideband make its mark and become accepted in amateur radio, so when experimenters needed help, it came in important ways.

Wes discussed the need for an improved audio phase shifter with both Don Norgaard and Robert Dome. The network designed by Norgaard was one geared to the amateur experimenter, and readily sacrificed ultimate performance for constructability by hams having limited access to precise-value components and well-calibrated test equipment. Both Norgaard and Dome agreed far better network performance was attainable but would require some added network complexity and significant number crunching to determine appropriate resistor and capacitor values.

Central's small engineering staff was already running at full throttle. While Wes' connections with Northwestern University could likely be pressed into service to develop the needed network, the learning curve might be a long, slow one. Why not ask the Stanford University radio club to see if anyone there would have interest in assisting? Stanford had been actively experimenting with single sideband since 1947; with them, there would be no learning curve. Perhaps such a study would be beneficial as a research project for those seeking an advanced degree.

In April 1955, Wes contacted Mike Villard and offered both a challenge and a reward for some enterprising engineering student: Develop a new phase shift network for Central Electronics and accept a brand new 20A exciter as payment in kind. Two Stanford students stepped up and accepted the challenge: Taylor Howard and Alfred Faries.

The two worked nonstop, clearly evident since they not only completed their network's initial paper design, computed exacting component values, and constructed test networks, but then they also completed an engineering paper describing their work's results by June—only three months, start to finish.

Howard and Faries earned their 20As. The result was excellent: a network capable of 50dB sideband suppression over the audio range of 160Hz to 3320Hz was deemed viable. To achieve this degree of performance, adherence to the team's calculated values—held with 0.3% tolerance—were necessary. With the electronics industry booming in the mid-1950s, getting component suppliers to supply parts at such tight tolerances was not unusual. In fact, the capacitors Central later used in its 100V phase shift network were guaranteed by the supplier to be within +0% and -0.2% of the values indicated on each supplied part!

Wes and Joe poured over the report and its findings and could find nothing outwardly wrong, yet wanted certainty this design made sense. Wes reached out to a friend at the RCA Corporation, Stuart (Stu) Seeley. Seeley's overall assessment was that the Stanford work was good; he suggested only a minor change to make the design a bit more flexible, and that was enough for Wes and Joe.

While there were never any B-versions of the 20A exciter produced by Central using the Stanford network, the young team's inspired work clearly made history in the eventual 100V and 200V transmitters. The PS-2 network, as it was later called, was paired with Batchelor's patent-pending balanced modulator and an exceedingly low-distortion (0.1%) dual channel audio system designed by Wes. The rest of the transmitter's design now boiled down to development of the heterodyne scheme for each band, packaging into a compact desktop cabinet and of course the design of the transmitters, many bandpass mixer, driver, and final amplifier couplers.

While by late 1956 the Central Electronics staff had grown to include two coil designers, a production supervisor, several product assembly people, and two engineering assistants, it was clearly not anything approaching a Hallicrafters or Collins-style operation. Central Electronics was a small operation with big time plans. It survived on cash flow, and that meant pushing out sellable products (20As, Slicers, and Warren stuff) during the day and pulling a second shift at night to design new products like the 100V.

The boys were burning the candle at both ends, time and circumstance steadily working against them.

Chapter 15: The Big Squeeze

Sales of Model 10A exciters started off modestly. Initially, it was through word of mouth. People heard Wes on the air with his sideband rig, would ask questions, and soon orders would come in via the US mail. There was never any issue with cash flow; it was instant. To buy a unit, the order included a money order. In those days, there were no credit cards. Sales were "cash on the barrel head."

The sales model gradually changed. As Wes began his travelling road show of educating hams at radio club meetings, hamfests, and tailgating swap meets, the sales were made on-site; when the stock of rigs on hand was exhausted, prepaid orders were accepted. But as ads in *QST* gained new individual ham interest, it also caught the attention of radio and electronics parts houses throughout the US. These places catered to the ham community, as those guys would usually buy parts locally.

Resistors, capacitors, switches, cabinets, tubes, relays...all the parts needed for homebrewed equipment were the normal fare of local parts suppliers, but now that commercially built equipment was becoming more popular during the post-war boom, some began carrying kit and pre-assembled ham gear as well.

Selling through dealers brought new challenges for small operations like Central Electronics. Each dealer expected to receive a discount for providing advertising and stocking the gear. Otherwise, why would they want the bother? Now, if a manufacturer suddenly had to provide a 20%

discount to accommodate a dealer level, he was faced with two options: accept a lower profit margin *or* raise prices. Raising the price of an existing product is a difficult decision to make. Doing so risks alienating prospective customers and tempering rather than growing business. Eating the dealer discount then means having to sell more radios to achieve the same net profit.

Central Electronics decided to gamble that it could sustain its profit goals by engaging dealers to build volume and reach more potential buyers than it could through *QST* ads or by mail order. Initially, that plan worked well; Central was selling all the exciters it could make. What they didn't consider fully, though, was market saturation. By the mid-1950s, the number of amateur radio licensees in the US was only around 130,000—and growing slowly. This ham radio hobby was an unusual one: a person had to pass difficult FCC Morse code and electronics theory examinations for access to the hobby. One could not simply buy equipment and operate. When weighted against the population of the Unites States then (170 million), to be fiscally viable Central Electronics and others would have to develop and market a continuous string of new products to entice a relatively small pool of prospective buyers. Eventually, Central would have to break out of just the ham radio market to remain relevant.

This is one reason why Central Electronics unveiled a product called Rejuva-Tube. Commercial television was finding a ready market in the US. Conceivably, every family would eventually have a television (or two) and service of those units would become a growth business. While television sets were loaded with tubes that would eventually wear out, those were generally inexpensive. The big exception was the picture tube.

The picture tube was the heart of all television sets. When it dimmed or outright failed its replacement was expensive, approaching 50% of the set's value. Joe Batchelor knew all about picture tubes woes since he and Jackie operated a home-grown radio and television business. As a ham who hated to throw anything away, he wondered if it would be possible to rejuvenate dimmed out picture tubes. After dissecting many dud tubes and identifying failure modes, he built a device that would clean up defective tubes, often restoring them to like-new functionality.

The best thing about Joe's idea was that his device simply plugged onto the picture tube's connector; no time consuming or expensive tube removal was required. In an hour's time, a television technician could restore a customer's picture tube, build goodwill, and secure a nice high-profit return for his trouble. Wes and Joe figured they could sell at least 20,000 of those devices to established repair shops and the wave of new ones springing up as television's acceptance grew. What's more, once color television became available, sales could skyrocket.

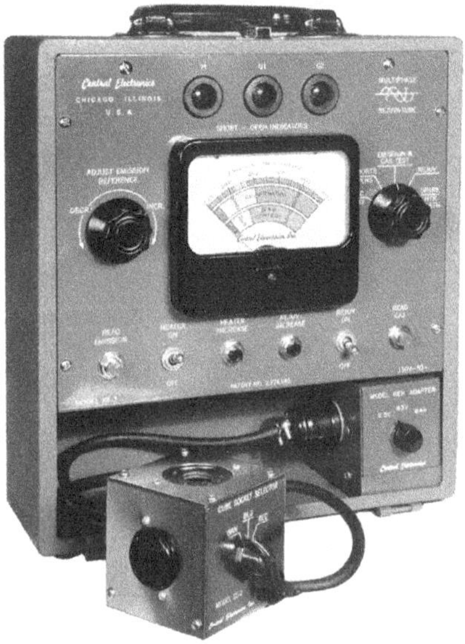

Rejuvatube

As 20As began rolling out of Central Electronics in 1954, so too did its new Rejuva-Tube. Those combined ham and television test equipment sales helped to moderate the blow that was to come. By the start of 1957, cracks were developing.

A small but growing number of ham dealers kept ordering ham gear on credit but were either slow to pay when sets were sold or simply went out of business and took the money with them! As the months went on,

Central saw its booked sales volume increase, but actual net profit level out—and then slowly decrease. Keep in mind, the funds to create new products like the 100V and others planned were funded by a portion of net profits. As those profits thinned, to keep the 100V's development moving, Wes had to dip into his personal savings.

This trend was also noticed by Tom Clemens. He had worked closely with Wes for years and could see the financial strain building. When offered an engineering manager's job at P&H Electronics in Lakeshore, Indiana that April, he accepted, principally to gain a bit more financial stability. At P&H, Tom's responsibility was to develop six-meter and two-meter transmitting converters and companion VHF linear amplifiers. Those products did not directly compete with work done at Central; and Tom, in leaving Central Electronics, agreed to never discuss the operation of the Batchelor broadband couplers.

By March of 1958, the problem had grown to an unsustainable level. There was no net profit and in fact the costs for running the business had sunk into deficit spending. Joe and Wes had completed the 100V prototype unit and had refined the design to what would have been a reproducible form, but lacked the funds to initiate, much less complete, the first run of several hundred radios. Worse was the realization that the lack of adequate funding had greatly delayed the new rig's introduction, which meant that once in production, the 100V would have to slug it out with many more competitors fighting for a portion of that small ham radio market.

Keep in mind, *QST* ads for the 100V transmitter and its planned accessories had been running since December 1957, building up intense interest in a product that had yet to come off the launching pad. Both men had forfeited their pay to keep essential personnel employed and accommodate vendors that absolutely had to be paid. The pressure on Central Electronics was building by the minute.

Wes began looking for what he called "a noble sire" to rescue Central Electronics and bring its revolutionary transmitter to market. He first contacted General Dynamics, who only had mild interest in the sideband concept. Next, Wes contacted George W. Borg of the Borg-Beck Company. While Borg-Beck was a Chicago firm that manufactured mechanical engine clutches at that time, it was also manufacturing electric clocks and other electronic devices used in automobiles. After a flurry of interest and due diligence, that trail eventually went cold. Wes had to keep looking.

Wes knew of Jim Burk, a fellow ham operator and owner of Standard Kollsman, Inc., and put out some feelers. Standard Kollsman was at that time deeply involved in the design and manufacture of television channel tuners, and open to new opportunities in the communications field. Upon learning more details about Central Electronics, particularly its growing number of important patents and inventions in the field of radio communications, Burk's interest grew.

Eventually negotiations for a buyout commenced with Kollsman's corporate attorney in New York. Initially, Schum's hopes were high for a lucrative agreement that would provide funds to cover construction costs for the new 100V transmitter, resolve outstanding claims from parts suppliers (who had been very patient with Central's slow treatment of past-due invoices), and give a reasonable return on the cash and sweat-equity investments the three Central stockholders (Schum, Warren and Batchelor) had shouldered while growing the business. Yet, after each meeting with the Kollsman's attorneys, the money Central's stockholders would receive diminished in $10,000 chunks. And $10,000 was a *lot* of money in 1957.

By the time the fourth and last Kollsman meeting occurred, the situation had become dire. Months had past, more debt had been accumulated by Central, and some suppliers were threatening to curtail parts shipments. After just a few minutes in the attorney's office, Schum had had enough. He shouted: "Over all of these months, you people have negotiated in bad faith. In each of these meetings, your sole focus has been to squeeze me to give up more. What you want is for the company's shareholders to *give* you our wonderful product, and that is *never* going to happen!"

With that, Wes slammed his briefcase shut, stormed out, and headed back to Chicago, angry at himself for being played for a fool. Schum would rather go down in bankruptcy with their 100V prototype perched on his or Joe's operating desk than *give* it away to corporate jackals.

A few days after cooling off, a friend suggested perhaps the Zenith Radio Corporation might have some interest and mentioned that he knew one of Zenith's co-founders, Karl Hassel. Hassel was a long-time ham operator, and so the two men were put in contact. It was Hassel who took the first step. He called Wes and the two briefly discussed the 100V concept. Sensing interest, Wes asked if Karl would like to see and operate the new transmitter. "Sure, Wes. Could you bring it over to my home?"

Wes was beyond excited. Karl, more than anyone, would understand how fantastic this new transmitter was, and see the potential it had in what was still a wide-open commercial, amateur, and defense communications marketplace. Joe and Wes gathered up their transmitter, along with enough parts and materials to connect to Karl's antenna farm—or, if his was lacking, to erect a suitable one for testing. There was no way Wes, Joe and the 100V were leaving Karl's house without having conducted a full-blown, on-air demonstration.

Karl Hassel was blown away.

Hassel had never seen a transmitter that could be operated in this manner, with no tuning except to net the radio on frequency...and the plethora of operating modes was simply unheard of. After an hour of operating, Hassel was hooked. Zenith wasn't just mildly interested in acquiring Central Electronics, Hassel would see to it that the deal was done and done fast.

Looking back, Wes remarked at how quickly it all happened. It was like magic. Within two weeks, Central Electronics had become a subsidiary of the Zenith Radio Corporation. The acquisition was made public on November 28th, 1958. All past-due supplier accounts were resolved, Central's stockholders received a fair payout, and plans were underway to move the 100V into immediate production. Wes became the new operation's vice president and Joe its engineering manager. A new and more expansive marketing plan would be crafted, and plans made to accelerate new products—such as a matching 100R receiver, and the big 2500L no-tune linear amplifier.

To bring those new plans and initiatives to fruition, the previously lean Central Electronics staff would have to be beefed up with more skilled assembly persons, specialized test equipment, more engineers, and more oversight. Central Electronics had gotten the steroid shot Wes and Joe believed was needed. And to add to the excitement of the year, Wes and Marge became the proud parents of daughter No. 4, Susan.

Ever hear someone lament, "Be careful what you ask for; you might just get it?" Schum and Batchelor likely had not. You see, the unintended downstream side effects of the Zenith buyout were beyond the two's imagination. At the end of three years, on January 1st, 1962 Central Electronics was suddenly out of the amateur radio business, with Joe Batchelor working for the Hallicrafters Corporation and Wes Schum scratching hard to recover.

Having spent fourteen years in educating hams on the virtues of single sideband at club meetings and conferences throughout the US, while developing groundbreaking products along the way, Wes had suddenly been ejected from the company he founded. Months before, he was betrayed by friend and fellow engineer Joe Batchelor. Zenith's abrupt exit from the market was one thing; Zenith's refusal to sell the amateur business back to him meant Wes had lost Central's important patent portfolio and was seemingly dead in the water.

While organizing Wes Schum's vast files that make up parts of this story's narrative, I came across a carefully saved letter that over the years likely gave him pause for reflection. Written by Barrie R. Barker, president of Barker & Williamson, Inc. and dated December 18, 1958, it sent a powerful, heartfelt message. B&W was then a highly respected manufacturer of radio transmission systems and parts, most notably its line of air-wound coils called Miniductor.

"I personally wish you the greatest measure of success in whatever you attempt. My greatest regret in your (Zenith Radio) consolidation lies in the fact that I did not know about it at an earlier enough date, because I can assure you that you would have found fertile ground for consolidation with our own company. That time is past, of course, but I should like to throw it in the pot anyway to give you an idea of our opinion of your company."

Is it any wonder Wes Schum avoided HF radio for nearly 25 years? He was too embarrassed to address the many unanswered questions about how it all unraveled. His Chicago-area ham friends were kind enough not to ask.

Chapter 16: The Sideband Wars

The early sideband on-air experiments had to have been a strange occurrence for hams operating AM. Absent a BFO and detecting AM phone via a simple diode detector, sideband signals must have sounded to those eavesdropping that aliens had landed from outer space!

The ARRL carried the water early in promoting the potential virtues of sideband to the ham community. The other prominent ham radio magazine then, CQ, took a more measured wait-and-see attitude. That more cautious stance made sense since in the late 1940s sideband test transmissions were typically at the high end of 75 meters and with few actual participants. Since so few were then experimenting with the new mode, there was little adverse interaction between AMers and Sidebanders.

By 1950, it was estimated that at most 300 hams throughout the US were then experimenting with single sideband, with 3970kHz and 3999kHz being favored nesting frequencies[9]. Just to put things in perspective, far fewer than 50% of licensed hams (then numbering 104,000 in the US) operated phone of any kind. Most hams communicated by CW[10]. Sideband's portion in number was clearly small, almost insignificant. But that did change—and in a big way.

---

9 Unpublished call sign listing of on-air sideband experimenters, compiled by Wes Schum.

10 CW was the primary mode used since most ham transmitters then were home constructed. CW transmitters operating the then-typical 50-watt to 200-watt power levels had few stages and were relatively easy to construct whereas AM transmitters were somewhat more complex and costly, by comparison.

Wes Schum could envision sideband as the spectrum-saver amateur and commercial radio services desperately needed. Since a large percentage of hams were also involved in radio on a commercial, professional basis then by selling hams on sideband, the sky would be the limit to its widespread acceptance.

He had to get into the game on its ground floor, and do it fast. Don Norgaard's SSB Jr. was the trigger point and soon Wes had a complete, inexpensive sideband transmission/reception package to sell. The best way to get the word out was to get it in front of groups of interested ham operators. That meant a sideband traveling road show, and Wes Schum became its master of ceremonies.

Wes began to seek club meetings in the Chicago-Milwaukee area where he could explain the theory of single sideband and how it could be copied[11] using conventional AM receivers. His first seminars were held in the spring of 1951. In response to those seminars, a small trickle of letters made their way to Central's Giddings Street operation. Soon orders for the early Model 10A arrived, again in a trickle, but a bit more with each successive theory presentation.

Next, Wes added actual demonstrations of single sideband; seeing and hearing is believing, right? Now, keep in mind when two or more AM stations tried to talk on the same frequency simultaneously, the result was a chaotic, noisy mess. Wes Schum's demonstrations would simply blow the audience away.

Two Model 10A exciters would be assembled on a desk. The two units would be crystal-controlled, but on the same center frequency. To silence any claim or trickery, Wes built an outboard crystal oscillator feeding the 10A, so one crystal, two transmitters, one carrier frequency. One 10A would have its upper sideband selected, the other its lower sideband.

A companion receiver was then equipped with one of Central's Model A sideband slicer units. This device would allow one to demodulate normal AM and each sideband individually.

11 Ham radio-speak for: demodulated.

IS SSB A BIG MYSTERY?

WHAT IS SSB? HOW DOES SSB WORK?

WHY DOES SSB WORK? WHAT CAN SSB DO?

NOW IS YOUR CHANCE

to SEE and HEAR how Single Sideband really works and to MEET THE MAN WHO KNOWS ALL THE ANSWERS

WES SCHUM, W9DYV
President
CENTRAL ELECTRONICS, INC., CHICAGO
Manufacturers of the 10B and 20A Multiphase exciters and other SSB equipment.

Wes will present a complete demonstration of SSB equipment and operating technique. Both phone and CW men who have attended demonstrations by Wes in other parts of the country say that his presentation is so outstanding that the amateurs in the St. Louis area can not afford to miss this great opportunity to learn about Single Sideband from the man who is the leader in the field. Wes will be glad to answer any questions which you may have in language which we all can understand.

TIME: 8:00 P.M. Thursday, October 28th
PLACE: DeSoto Room, 16th FLoor (Capacity 550 People)
HOTEL DeSOTO, 11th & Locust Streets
(Downtown St. Louis)

Prizes — Free Refreshments

BCNU - BILL DuBORD, WØQDF
Sponsored by WALTER ASHE RADIO CO.

Sideband demo announcement

SINGLE
SIDEBAND
DEMONSTRATION

8 PM WEDNESDAY JUNE 15, 1955

Wesley R. Schum, W9DYV, President of Central Electronics, will operate two SSB transmitters on the same frequency using opposite sidebands - without interference. A simple presentation of the generation, amplification and reception of SSB signals.

DADE RADIO CLUB
AMERICAN RED CROSS BUILDING
5020 BISCAYNE BOULEVARD
MIAMI, FLORIDA

DOOR PRIZE! New Central Electronics "Q" Multiplier

Wes Schum's speaking announcement

First, he would operate one 10A and then the other in normal AM/double sideband mode, to prove to the audience that the same information in an AM signal was contained in both sidebands and that the equipment was properly configured. Then, he would set one 10A exciter to upper sideband mode and the other to lower sideband mode.

That was the time Wes would ask for two volunteers who would dutifully become part of the demonstration. Each volunteer would be handed a microphone from the two exciters, and would then be asked to speak. By selecting the upper or lower sideband via the Slicer, the audience would hear the two individual volunteers, totally absent of interference! Two separate sideband conversations could be had in the space of one AM signal.

That did it. Once the first of those demonstration was made in 1951 at the Starved Rock Hamfest, instead of mere trickles of orders they became a babbling brook, a small stream, and ultimately a torrent.

Model 10A kits and assembled units were flying out of the Giddings Street garage operation, and a move to Belmont Street became mandatory. Wes Schum was in the sideband business in a big way. Invitations to speak at local hamfests, ARRL conventions, and regional shows began pouring in. To name a handful, the '54 and '55 Dayton Hamfest at the Biltmore, the '53 Delta Division Conference in New Orleans, the '55 SPARC Convention in St. Petersburg, the '54 New England ARRL Convention, the '55 Pacific Division Convention, and the '55 Oregon Annual Convention.

During the years of 1951 through 1960, Wes Schum gave over 100 workshops and demonstrations on the virtues of single sideband. At one 1957 conference Dick Bellew, then the amateur radio division's sales manager for Collins Radio, muttered, "I do believe Wes Schum could sell snow to the Eskimos!" What endeared Wes to the amateur community was his tireless energy and ability to explain complex single sideband theory with language and examples that satisfied both technically savvy and hobby operators alike. He made the concepts of phasing, RF linearity, interference rejection, and audio quality come alive, and excited people to give sideband a try.

This is how Wes Schum earned the title *Mr. Sideband.* In fact, some letters mailed to him at the Belmont factory were addressed that way! Of course, Wes was not alone in aggressively marketing sideband. But if he wasn't the first to do so, he most certainly was the most effective. Soon, the improved 20A and 10B exciters, along with the broadband 600L amplifier and signal monitoring oscilloscopes (Model MM-1 and MM-2) were flying out of the Belmont Avenue shop.

It seemed by 1956 that single sideband was on fire, with Wes Schum and others pouring on the coals. Collins Radio had unveiled its impressive KWS-1/75A-4 "gold dust twins" transmitter and receiver combination. Hallicrafters had its HT-32. EF Johnson had unveiled its new Pacemaker transmitter. Amateur sideband enthusiast groups were springing up throughout the US. Many of those would go on to host mini-conferences, operating events, and sideband dinners.

Wes Schum and Joe Batchelor—Sideband demonstration

Wes Schum and early SSB demonstration in 1953

50's SSB Field Day

50's SSB Field Day

20A in use

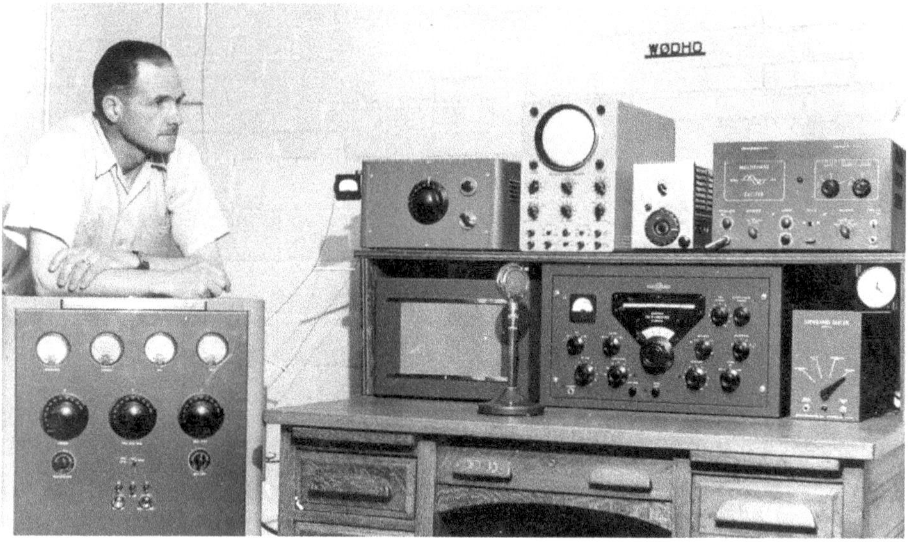

Harland Dewitz 1952

100V 600L station

The Sidebander Magazine

Sideband Dinner 1955

Chicago Sideband Dinner 1956

New York Sideband Dinner 1956

Wes Schum receives the "Sideband Suzy" Award

In viewing photographs of those gatherings, one thing is clear: those sideband gatherings were high class events! Forget the blue jeans, tee shirts, and grass-cuttin' clothes that show up at today's typical hamfest. Oh, no. *Everyone* wore suites and ties—and for the YLs/XYLs, a stylish dinner dress—at those sideband events! Sideband had become big time radio!

Now, one might think that this new sideband stuff was fully embraced with smiles and open arms by the multitudes. It was surely the answer to the phone man's dreams, right?

Well, guess again.

No, a large contingent of AM operators then detested everything about sideband. "Argh...this sounds like Donald Duck garbage!" "If this stuff is so great, why is that clown splattering 30kHz up and down the band!" "My grass stopped growing—must be that sideband disease." "Those inconsiderate sidebanders are interfering with our ability to talk anywhere in the band!" "Let's go pin that sideband guy's coax so he blows his final and shuts down!"

Those are some of the *nice* comments!

Simply reading letters sent in by irate hams to the various magazines or speaking with old timers from that era gives perspective of the uphill battle those hearty purveyors of single sideband gallantly faced. In the November 1948 issue of CQ magazine, W1BGJ wrote:

"Is our present investment (AM) to be thrown in the waste can? We have been threatened with NBFM, pulse transmission, TVI, and now SSSC! If SSSC is so potent, why do not the broadcast stations use it? Why do not the shortwave stations use it! If some of the boys want to use SSSC or whatever, let them go to it. But please don't try to reform everyone else."

In the May 1953 issue of *QST*, one reader commented:

> "I was startled to learn from the January issue that there are only 237 hams operating on single sideband in the US. Even though you have plugged the cause with page after monotonous page of explanatory and construction articles and have even maintained a regular SSB department in *QST*, you have cajoled only 1/50th of 1% of the licensed amateurs in this tedious pursuit. If there is a dedicated group who feel that the electronic future of the world rests upon their humped shoulders, let them do what they wish with SSB. But please, *QST*, don't jam it down the throats of us ordinary citizens."

Comments like those in magazine letters and at club meetings eventually spread to on-air open warfare, with deliberate interference being the weapon of choice. A letter from W4WQT, as contained in the December 1954 issue of *QST*, clearly illustrates the type on-air SSB vs AM battles held nightly on 75 meters.

> "Fellow single-sideband operators, please don't let the actions of so few double-sideband (AM) operators cause you to become numbskulls also. Remember, you hold the 'big stick;' so why use it to destroy an old-fashioned double sideband net just because a few carriers bother you? The point is that the action of a very few double sideband operators in deliberately trying (if they only knew how helpless they are) to QRM the Interstate Sideband Net is causing a few sideband boys to 'pay 'em back' by destroying the Trans-Continental Phone Net (3975kHz) and the Tennessee Phone Net (3980kHz). Knowing full well, through much experience, you can't tell a double-sideband die-hard anything..."

The animosity between the two forms of radiotelephony became so acute that a movement to create segregated AM and SSB sub-bands was once proposed. That brilliant concept only served to further fuel the fires of animosity, particularly since the sub-band concept would have allocated the same-sized spectrum slivers for AM and SSB operations. The dead-on-arrival sub-band idea only served to make matters worse between the two sets of advocates: AMers argued (correctly) that if sideband was so spectrally efficient and legions more AM versus sideband stations were active, why should sideband get so much relative space? They should be able to do more with less, right? Sidebanders argued station numbers would quickly change, to the point where twice as many sidebanders would be active versus AMers, so the proposed segments were fine. And so it went, a back-and-forth war of words.

The FCC ultimately weighed in and summarily refused to consider a sub-band concept. The two modes were both forms of amplitude modulation and would have to find a way to coexist. Ultimately, over the next decade, sideband gained its predicted widespread acceptance and the controversy died out...sort of.

Now you understand the type of general audience Wes Schum faced in the early 1950s while giving those important sideband seminars. A large portion of any given audience wanted to learn and were interested in this exciting, new technology—while a troublesome other group might join in only to cause a ruckus.

Nothing they did ever bothered Wes Schum.

Always armed with the facts, a steel-trap mind, and a powerful set of wits, Wes commanded the show. In fact, he enjoyed the occasional sparring with sideband disbelievers. While some may have entered those sessions with animosity in their hearts, most left with a far different attitude. Some hardballers shocked their AM pals by ordering Central Electronics exciters!

While conducting his demonstration and answering questions about sideband at the 1952 Lithia Springs Convention in the Atlanta area, Schum was accosted by two huge 250-pound Georgian AM heavyweights. "Wes, we have listened to all of this sideband nonsense, and seen your demonstration. AM is the *superior* mode. We intend to immerse you in Lithia Springs and cleanse you of this sideband nonsense!" they exclaimed.

The two grabbed Wes under his shoulders, lifted him up, and carried him to nearby Lithia Springs. The whole meeting room emptied out and followed to witness this sideband exorcism. Now, normally, having a guy immersed in a creek would have been a huge cause for concern, but Lithia Springs at that spot was just a small trickle: at most two feet wide, and only inches deep.

The pair briefly dipped Wes' feet into the Spring, then lifted him up and deposited his dripping feet onto the creek bank. The crowd broke into loud applause once Wes was back on solid ground. Collecting his thoughts as the clapping died down, Wes looked at the two "exorcists" and boomed, "You *must* give up on that AM *nonsense*! Sideband is the wave of the future, and you need to get on it *now*—or get cast aside!"

The two sideband disbelievers bowed their heads in thoroughly mocked shame. Suddenly, a fellow sidebander sprang forward from the crowd—unable to contain himself, no doubt—and kissed Wes on the forehead, whereupon the gathered crowd exploded in laughter!

Eventually, the two radiotelephony modes did learn to coexist; a voluntary gentleman's agreement came to pass, under which those who wished to experiment with sideband could, in concept, operate without interference from AMers. That agreement was so successfully employed in the late 1950s and early '60s that similar voluntary segments were gradually fashioned by the amateur community for other important modes, such as slow-scan television, RTTY, and more. So, for a long while, the AM v. sideband confrontations (on air and in person) died away, except for the occasional knucklehead.

Oddly, with the advent of today's modern multimode software defined radios that fundamentally use the phasing principle, a resurgence of AM operation is occurring. Of course, all the technical aspects for why sideband is the superior transmission mode remain, but a strong AM signal, with its wide broadcast-like frequency response, just sounds good!

Indeed, everything old becomes new again, given enough time.

Chapter 17: The Zenith Years: The Good, the Bad, the Ugly

Almost as soon as the ink had dried on the Central Electronics buyout agreement, Zenith sprang into action. Zenith understood the dilemma Wes had faced with a backlog of booked sales: a tidal wave of buyer interest, but no product to ship. Joe and Wes had, in theory, developed a reasonable approach to building its extraordinarily complex 100V product. The plan was to break the 100V down into plug-together subassemblies that could be more efficiently built in a production line format. Once a backlog of constructed and tested modules was ready, these would then be assembled into a complete transmitter unit. The module groupings would include power supply, VFO, sideband generator, wiring harnesses, speech amplifier/relay assembly, RF chassis, low-level coil sets, and high-level output couplers.

Central's highly competent but somewhat eccentric draftsman, Arnold Walder, was tasked with developing the many detailed component part images, assembly drawings, and schematic diagrams needed for the 100V. Walder had long been associated with Wes since the days of Cover Dual-Signal and instinctively knew the level of drawing quality and detail required.

As Wes put it, Arnold Walder was a crusty, tobacco-chewing, highly opinionated, no-nonsense character. He formerly painted houses for a living but was also a super artist. Considerably older than the fellows at Cover and exempt from the draft, Walder wanted to do his part to help win the war. Although having never worked as an electronics draftsman, he figured it was nothing more than another form of art, so why not give it a shot? Turned out that Walder held a latent talent for making electronic drawings flow in a logical, easy to understand format.

Zenith's management team was not as impressed. Aside from the character stuff, Walder was 70 years old in 1958, and beyond Zenith's normal service age. As far as Zenith was concerned, age 65 was an appropriate age for personnel to retire. Schum was not having it. "What difference does age make to a draftsman? If you can find me a man that can provide the same quality of artwork as Arnold, and do it in the time he can, then let's see what you have. I've dealt with many other draftsmen and know you can't get anywhere near this quality for the salary I'm paying Arnold."

Zenith relented. "Well, under the circumstances Wes, and what you believe Walder can accomplish here, perhaps he should stay on."

He did; in fact, he remained on the Central Electronics team for not only the 100V, but the 200V and other projects. Wes Schum always went to bat for people he knew were competent and had the Company's best interests at heart. Age was just a number.

Wes fought and succeeded in keeping his enter team intact after the Zenith buyout. Joe Batchelor continued as the core engineering team. Frank Schwartz, who was Joe's lab assistant carried over. Schwartz was not a radio engineer, but a highly capable technician with excellent mechanical assembly skills. Dick Vernell, who joined Central when it was located at Wes' garage on Giddings Street had progressed from parts gofer to Central's parts buyer and stocking manager. Over the years, he had developed excellent relations with Chicago-area materials and parts suppliers. He, more than anyone, had managed to keep the vendors at bay during the Company's cash flow difficulties. His job carried over with the buyout. Nick Fishik remained as Central's chief model maker.

Wes Schum in office at Central Electronics

Zenith had made a point to keep its direct interference in Central's operation somewhat at arm's length, but for good reason: Central Electronics was a non-union shop, an anomaly for a Chicago-based electronics manufacturing operation. There is a humorous story of how that came to pass.

"I was sitting in my office, going over some drawing recently completed by Arnold when my secretary buzzed the intercom. 'Wes, there is a rather large man here that wants to talk about unionization. What should I do?' Oh, send him in and I'll get rid of him."

Wes had a very dim view of unions. He believed that if a company treated its employees with respect, paid them a reasonable wage, and provided a wholesome working environment, then what could a union do, other than add costs and drive a wedge between workers and management? Wes always looked out for his people and paid them an above average wage for the services they provided. Even while he was being squeezed by creditors and past due accounts, he never held back employee pay. So, what did this union guy want and why?

Keep in mind, Wes was not a large man by any stretch. He was 5 ft. 7 inches tall and weighed about 160 pounds. When the union man came through the doorway, it was as if the lights in the office had dimmed. He was indeed huge: maybe 300 pounds, well over 6 feet tall, and with a neck about the diameter of a steering wheel. No wonder the secretary was intimidated.

Not Wes Schum.

Wes calmly looked up from his seat and asked, "Well, what do *you* want?"

The Hulk responded: "I wanna talk to the workers about organizing a union here! My job is to protect their interests."

Wes responded: "I'm already taking care of those interests, so what more can you do?"

The Hulk: "That's not your concern, Schum. I wanna talk to the workers, *now*!"

Wes was not impressed nor intimidated. He calmly replied, "You aren't talking to anyone here while I'm paying them to work. You can figure something out when they knock off."

"OK, I'll speak to them here during their lunch break!" the Hulk exclaimed.

Wes shook his head. "Wrong again, pal. I pay for their time at lunch. Take it to the street or your place, after work. Now, get out!"

The Hulk did in fact leave, but only after giving Wes a hard stare that would have burned holes into battleship armor. He slammed the office door and stormed off. The Hulk did in fact hold a series of meeting with the employees off site and referred to Wes as a Judas selling them out for his own personal gain.

Apparently, the Hulk was winning the employees over as the next week they asked for a company meeting with Wes. Perhaps he was a Judas?

Wes calmly listened to everyone's opinion and why they thought a union was good for the worker. When all had finished, he then asked to speak:

"I am not going to attempt to influence your vote on this unionization idea. Only, please keep this in mind: What Judas-minded businessman do you know who would have stopped paying himself so he could pay his workers? Or pay a medical expense when others likely would not? Would a Judas fight to keep you employed here after Zenith bought the firm? Would a Judas push to gain each of you wage increases as I have? So, what exactly will a union provide for you—for the union dues you will be expected to pay—that you aren't already now receiving? Who's the real Judas here?"

Wes then left the assembly floor, returning to his office. Before a moment passed to comfortably sit at his desk, the employees had already voted: NO UNION. Is it any wonder Zenith gave Wes a wide berth at Central Electronics? Here was a young, exceptionally talented man who could not be intimidated by *anyone*.

No, Zenith was content to provide Central Electronics with the resources to get the 100V project and others done, and to later assess the market's depth. Yet, Zenith insisted that Central should adopt Zenith management and accounting practices so that the new subsidiary's contributions could be weighed against the operation's core entertainment and defense industry operations.

To expedite the 100V's entrance into the production phase, Zenith added engineering and manufacturing talent from its television group. As it turned out, Zenith's color television engineering department had progressed well ahead of its planned start of color TV manufacturing. Some of those engineers had a lull in workload and were temporarily loaned to Central. Important Zenith names who provided key assistance were Charles (Charlie) Heuer, Dillard Carr, Ed Miller, Herb Saxton, Phil Sijerski, Nick Vrabel, Bert Galler, Ray Sermon, Grant Macinson, and Jim Clark.

Nick Vrabel's contribution was near immediate—and critical. Vrabel was a long-time Zenith production foreman. His job at Zenith had been to find and implement production line refinements geared to higher productivity. When inspecting Central's production floor, he was shocked at how long the floor workers were taking to assemble the relatively simple and uncomplicated Rejuva-Tube product. Ten people were tasked with producing Rejuva-Tube, but their best daily yield was a paltry twelve completed units.

Vrabel carefully studied the team's workflow and identified many time-wasting bottlenecks. Working with Arnold Walder, improved sets of Rejuva-Tube assembly drawings were prepared. Next, the parts needed for Rejuva-Tube assembly were pre-kitted to match the new streamlined assembly steps, taking the guesswork out of selecting the right components for a given task. Vrabel and Arnold trained the assembly teams and pushed to focus their activities by the minute. Now, Vrabel was a somewhat imposing figure with a huge, booming voice that could rattle windows up and down West Belmont Avenue. When he spoke, he had everyone's undivided attention.

Soon, Rejuva-Tube daily production grew from 12 units to as many as 50! The problem was no longer production, but shipping. Vrabel zeroed in on improving the shipping department's processes to match the new production efficiencies. Pallets of Rejuva-Tube containers were soon piling up on Central's railway dock for shipment by Railway Express throughout the USA. Wes and Joe would often find themselves looking out at the assembly floor in awe. That Nick Vrabel knew his stuff!

While Rejuva-Tubes were flying out the back door, another portion of the Belmont building was being configured for 100V production, with Nick Vrabel doing his magic. The coil department, now managed by Ed Miller, was likewise expanded, since many plug-in coil assemblies would be needed in the new 100V. A total of five plug-in units were required for each 100V: the VFO doubler, heterodyne oscillator, first and second mixer stages, and the driver output. Each of these had several smaller single tuned or bandpass-tuned RF transformers using single-layer or universal style windings.

Miller secured multiple George Stevens coil winders from Zenith's huge tool inventory stock and configured those into coil winding stations, one for each type of coil module. A special set of machinist lathes, with attachment jigs designed by Nick Fishik, were provisioned into winders for the Batchelor output couplers. The heavier wire sizes used in the Batchelor couplers, as compared to the 28 to 32-gauge wire used in the plug-in units, were beyond the capability of the smaller, precision Stevens winders. The lathe-crafted coil winding machines were perfectly suited for the task.

Finally, specially configured test sets were built to verify the functionality of completed module assemblies. Since the various 100V modules were connectorized, it was a straightforward matter of connecting a module to its allied test set, via an umbilical connector cord, and to then run through a precise set of verification and alignment steps. Light indicators provided a go/no-go indication of verification success or failure. There was even a special room established to test and temperature-compensate 100V VFO units. As many as ten VFOs could be simultaneously monitored for temperature drift characteristics. Operators became so adept at testing how 100V VFOs performed that upon viewing a VFO's initial frequency drift rate, an operator could instinctively derive which added compensation capacitor components would be necessary.

Central Electronics VFO Lab

Dillard Carr – Sideband Module Testing

CE Belmont Stree Model Shop

Once 100V production commenced in February 1959, a big problem became apparent.

Mad as a hornet, Vrabel burst into Wes' office on a dismal Monday morning. "Wes, we have a damned big problem. The place is flooded with completed 100Vs, but we can't ship a damned thing. The Batchelor couplers are screwed up. Ed Miller's group is circling the drain. They can't reproduce the damned things!"

Wes was afraid of this. It was like a replay of the problems he and Tom Clemens encountered and fought through with the 600L amplifier's launch and its Batchelor couplers. The Batchelor couplers worked well, individually, but when trying to apply production manufacturing techniques and the tolerance variations those processes introduce, it all spelled trouble. The manufacturing part could eventually be fixed, but that would take time they really didn't have. The natives were getting restless. Dealers had been calling daily, trying to gain some sense of their 100V demo deliveries, not to mention letters and telephone calls from inquiring ham operators eager to buy.

Wes paused for a moment, collected his thoughts and asked, "OK, Nick, do you know *anyone* at Zenith that can figure out what the hell's going wrong here? And do it fast?"

Nick did. He made some telephone calls, and the next day Zenith's Charles (Charlie) Heuer was knocking on Central's front door. Heuer was a brilliant television engineer, and author of numerous television patents. What he could contribute was a firm grasp of network theory and how to apply that to manufacturing practice. After a week of examining Batchelor couplers, Heuer sensed the couplers would be highly efficient and most practical—eventually. Yet, getting them to yield that potential would take time that they didn't have. Perhaps he could design a simplified output coupler as an interim solution. His would not have the steep-sided response or as deep a harmonic rejection as the Bachelor couplers, but as Nick put it, "Wes, beggars can't be choosers. We have to do something *now*!"

Wes agreed, and Heuer was given the green light to proceed. The Heuer Couplers, as they were called, were essentially the RF equivalent o autotransformers. They proved simple to construct but unlike the Batchelor couplers, these included ferrite tuning and fixed coupling capacitors. Fortunately, they were compact in size and could be constructed using the same coil forms as the Batchelor ones; in short, Charlie Heuer had crafted a viable set of plug-in replacements. Approximately 150 of the first 100V transmitters were shipped with Heuer couplers. The Batchelor couplers were seamlessly integrated into 100V production once all the manufacturing issues had been resolved by Ed Miller's team.

So, was the Batchelor Coupler the only problem that delayed 100V production? Unfortunately, no.

The first sets of heterodyne crystals needed for the 100V transmitter failed to meet Central's drift specifications and were rejected. A new supplier, Northwestern Engineering Labs, was later retained and that problem solved. Then there was an initial problem with the main VFO capacitors. This, too, was resolved by Centralab, who designed a special, high stability mica capacitor for Central's VFO that included several parallel-connected units within one hermetically sealed housing. And so it went.

One by one, initial production problems were resolved. Yet from the vantage point of today and considering Central had to quickly become integrated into the Zenith behemoth—which at the time was the largest manufacturer of entertainment radio, high-fidelity and television equipment in the US—getting 100V production fully established in under six months was a remarkable achievement.

The first 100Vs were sent to dealers to get units before the buying public. A condition of sending those initial units to dealers was that they could not immediately be sold to the public. The dealers were required to make those first sets operational at their facilities and to report back any observed quality issues for resolution before 100Vs were to be delivered in numbers; Zenith had its "The quality goes in before the name goes on" reputation to protect.

Once in the field, two problems cropped up. Neither one stopped initial supply of 100Vs to the buying public, but they did require downstream corrective action. The first involved frequency drift: not from the VFO, where one might expect it, but from the crystal controlled heterodyne oscillators. The Batchelor-designed heterodyne oscillator subjected crystals to relatively high crystal current; the resultant heat in the crystals caused slow changes in operating frequency.

Unfortunately, that was not the initial drift source identified by Batchelor and associates as the reports drifted in (no pun intended). The biggest drift contributor at first appeared to be heat rise from adjacent tubes and its effect on per-band oscillator output coils. The team's initial fix was the installation of temperature compensation capacitors. That substantially slowed the frequency drift, but there remained some residual long-term drifting. That's when the oscillator itself went under the microscope. This long-term drift was corrected in the next 100V production run and a further refined oscillator design coupled with the ability to add heat-stabilized crystal ovens became part of the eventual 200V transmitter.

Sporadic reports of spurious transmitted emissions from some, but not all, 100V transmitters dropped on Wes' desk. The solution to this ailment required the installation of voltage trimming potentiometers on the first and second mixer stages. This modification was first announced as a field-change for sold units, and later incorporated into new production sets. The 200V transmitter gained newly introduced frame grid mixer tubes from Amperex that further improved spurious signal rejection.

Perhaps these sorts of anomalies can be expected whenever a product breaks barriers and is so new in concept. Yet product engineers, Batchelor's team, would have been expected to punish their designs and root those problems out before the equipment left the factory. Zenith, to its credit, spared no effort or expense in not only bringing the 100V and 200V to market, but also in encouraging continuous improvement to each model as new components or processes became viable. They, like Wes Schum, wanted only the best equipment to bear the Central Electronics-Zenith Radio name.

Soon, the 100V and later the 200V transmitters were outselling all the competitors. Those no-tune feature-rich rigs had formed a kind of cult following and drew pileups whenever one appeared on air. To be sure, it was an expensive, high-end radio. Few had seen one up close (not nearly as many hamfests then as today), and of course, the instant-access electronic information age was decades away. While everyone at Central Electronics was thrilled its long-delayed product had finally become a reality and was selling beyond expectation, no one sensed the oncoming tsunami.

Production of the 200V transmitter was initiated in 1961, and Zenith's color television business was exploding. People had been waiting years for Zenith to enter the color television fray, but its management was committed to waiting until a reasonable amount of color programming was available to make color television production viable. The programming market must first grow to a point where people have a reason and willingness to spend money for far more complex and expensive color sets. Zenith wanted a sure thing, and it got one; by 1960, color television was finding its way.

As 1961 ended, Zenith management (then President Hugh Robertson) was busy scrutinizing the numbers. Zenith was closing in on over $270 million dollars of television sales. By contrast, Central Electronics' sales volume was around $2 to 3 million while also carrying a heavy research and development load for planned new products.

Whereas single sideband was becoming a mainstay in the defense communications market, Zenith had done virtually nothing to claw its way in. The important relationships Zenith needed to develop a market there for its sideband gear were near zero. The Company's attention had been focused on the huge television market, fueled by color television's arrival. Could Zenith find opportunity in the maritime or commercial communications marketplace? Yes, but not right now: Zenith had to strike while color television was going like gangbusters.

Robertson gathered the various members of Zenith's management team over the Thanksgiving holiday. Their decision, after sifting through the numbers, was to have Central Electronics immediately exit the amateur radio market.

Zenith, a year earlier, had committed to building a new plant for Central Electronics in Paris, Illinois. Located 160 miles south of Chicago, the new facility was being constructed to accommodate 500 workers. By the time the 100V transmitter began to ship, Zenith had planned for Central Electronics to build not only its amateur radio line at this new Paris facility, but also Zenith's hearing aids and stereophonic entertainment gear. Work on the facility was nearing conclusion, and the Schums were already making plans to put their home on the market.

1962 was looking to be a wonderful year for Central Electronics.

So, it came as no surprise when Wes was invited to an important, hastily scheduled management meeting the morning of December 4th. Three months prior, he had been requested to have his operation prepare engineering samples and cost projections for products Central envisioned to be produced in 1962. He guessed the head honchos were now ready to hear about those new plans and products.

Armed and ready to answer any technical and cost questions, Wes entered the meeting that Monday morning with great confidence. He had spent the entire weekend polishing the facts and putting his materials in order.

By Monday at 9 a.m., Wes had confidently entered the downtown Zenith conference room, sat down, opened his files, and was preparing to make his presentation.

He was stopped cold when Robertson opened the meeting. "Wes, thank you for coming here today. I know you are prepared to discuss new products and costs with us, but that's not why we asked you in. You see, the management team met after Thanksgiving, and we have determined Zenith should exit the sideband radio business. When a business is doing nearly two hundred seventy million in annual sales, it needs another two or three million like a hole in the head, especially if it takes so much of our time to administer. We need you to have the operation's business closed by December thirty-first. Zenith will retain your services until February twenty-eighth. Wes, you have done all that we have asked of you. It is nothing personal, only a business decision. I hope you understand."

Wes was frozen, in shock. Did he hear that right?

For someone who was always ready to speak, Schum was struck silent. He couldn't utter a sound. His emotions were all over the map. How could he explain this to the workers? Or Central's many dealers? How was he going to break this news to Marge and the children? How could he have not seen this coming and prepared for it? By then, the couple had four young daughters and a bread winner soon to be absent the *bread*.

What next? Everything he had worked all those years for, suddenly gone in an instant.

Robertson, sensing how the news had startled Wes, directed the management team to take a 30-minute break so Wes could collect his thoughts.

Upon their return, Wes had somewhat recovered and asked only a few questions.

Did Zenith intend to have Central Electronics file for bankruptcy? "No, the firm will continue as a subsidiary, because Zenith intends to relocate it to the new Paris facility and use its non-union status to construct hearing aid and stereo systems, and also color television test equipment for use by Zenith repair service stations."

"OK, so can I buy the amateur radio portion of the business?"

"No. We intend to take the loss on Zenith's corporate taxes."

"OK, so can I at least buy back the Batchelor broadband coupler patent?"

"No Wes, it may be useful to Zenith in the design of future color televisions or we may attempt at some point to enter the military market. The patents Central was granted, that Zenith owns, are important to us."

"So, what you are doing is telling me that I am on my own, to sink or swim."

"Now Wes, you built your company from an idea. You are a bright young man and no doubt have many more ideas and products to contribute. You'll be fine."

It took every bit of self-control for Wes Schum not to tell them exactly what those titans of industry could do with their color televisions and their cavalier treatment of his team. Inside, he was on fire. But he said nothing, and quietly exited the room without looking at anyone. He had a family to consider. Christmas was in a few weeks. How could he hurt his children by lashing back? Sure, he was deeply hurt, but lots of people get hurt. He needed Zenith's money, as little as was coming his way, to get through the holidays and to start his new venture...whatever that could possibly be, on such short notice.

Back at Central that afternoon, he called a company meeting and informed the workers that the Company was changing; it was no longer in the amateur radio business. Some would be offered positions in Paris, Illinois. Some, such as Dillard Carr, Nick Fishik, Roy Sherman, Nick Vrabel, and others, would be absorbed into Zenith's massive television operation.

Wes Schum was soon to be on his own and scrambling to figure out what to do next. Trying to pull together a potential team to develop new product ideas, he renewed contact with Tom Clemens. At that time, Tom was no longer employed by P&H, but had landed with the Hallicrafters Corporation. How he was "recruited" from P&H Electronics to Hallicrafters is an interesting story in itself.

P&H, Central, Hallicrafters and others were attending a single sideband conference in Wisconsin in 1959. For this trip, Tom brought along his new then-new wife, as the conference was being held at a high-end downtown Milwaukee hotel. It was mid-summer, and the hotel had a rooftop swimming pool. As it turned out, Mrs. Clemens had decided to go swimming and was equipped with her brand new, very skimpy bikini. Then, the bikini had recently become a huge fashion statement; it even had its own song by Brian Hyland. Now, Tom's wife was a few years younger than he and very, very well-endowed.

She filled that itsy bitsy bikini to the max.

Also interested in an afternoon swim was Bill Halligan. The two didn't know each other but arrived at the pool about the same time. Tom's wife jumped into the pool's deep end and was in immediate trouble. It was not that she couldn't swim, but that her bikini top had launched itself off her body. She was topless and in distress! Halligan, gentleman that he was, came to the rescue with a towel and magnanimously dove in to retrieve the detached bikini top.

Once recovered and on dry land, they began to chat. She explained that her husband was a radio engineer involved with the conference and out of curiosity, Bill asked about him. When she mentioned his name was Tom, and he worked for P&H, Bill's eyes widened. "By chance, your husband isn't Tom *Clemens*, is he?"

"Why, yes," she responded.

"Oh! My company had been trying to hire your husband away from Wes Schum at Central Electronics for over two years, and even trailed him after he moved to P&H, but Tom won't even talk to us!"

Wife: "Really? How much are you offering him to jump?"

Halligan, without a hint of hesitation, declared, "Twice his current salary!"

Wife: "Sold! He'll be at your office on Monday! Now, where is it?"

True to her word, Tom Clemens, formerly of Central Electronics and P&H Electronics, reported for duty at Hallicrafters' plant on Kostner Avenue the following Monday morning. Wes and Bill Halligan were friendly competitors and enjoyed occasional visits at the various conferences. The two had a goodhearted laugh over Bill's recruitment of W9OKA.

Wes, though, was proud of Tom's growth in the Industry and the reputation he had built. He had joined Central as a young man with incredible drive and like Wes, had bootstrapped himself into a self-educated radio engineer. Tom later earned a degree in electrical engineering and authored patents involving antenna systems.

By June 1960, Joe Batchelor had left Central Electronics while severing ties with his long-time ham friend and business partner Wes. Unlike the departure of Tom Clemens, this was not to be a friendly parting of company. The pressure associated with getting the 100V to market put stress on the men's friendship. That Joe failed to prevent the broadband coupler yield problems in the first place rubbed Wes and others raw.

Joe Batchelor was a brilliant engineer, but his one flaw was he could never get projects fully completed. Wes, Tom Clemens, or someone else often had to step in, as otherwise Joe's work would never be done. And worse, while Joe's ideas were top shelf, they were often loosely configured and difficult for anyone to reproduce.

It is one thing to build one device and get it to work; it is an altogether different matter to make hundreds or thousands of a device and have them work reliably. That was the talent Wes, Tom, and others from Zenith brought to the table. Yet the "interference" bothered Joe. He didn't need anyone's help; he was the MENSA guy. It was Joe's patents that were behind the 100V. There would be no Central Electronics, had it not been for Joe Batchelor—at least, according to Joe.

For whatever reason, Joe Batchelor didn't feel appreciated. So, what happened became a one-man underground campaign to have Schum tossed aside. Character rumors and innuendo about Schum being propagated by Batchelor eventually caught the attention of senior engineering managers at Zenith.

Highly experienced Zenith department leaders such as Ed Passow, Bill Van Slyck, and others knew the two men, their contributions, personalities, and character. The rumors didn't match reality. No matter how brilliant a person might be, Zenith had no tolerance for troublemakers. Zenith's management made clear that Wes Schum was the only principal at Zenith's subsidiary, and after weighing the damage caused, suggested that Batchelor consider a job change—soon. Joe did leave not long after; he landed, as did Tom Clemens, at Hallicrafters.

It wasn't until the mid-1990s that Schum and Batchelor reconciled their differences, after a fashion. Oddly enough, it was a chance observation made during work in 1957 while researching new methods for developing single sideband that led the two to repair their fractured friendship as older men. According to Wes and others interviewed about those difficult times, people were frustrated and upset by the many 100V production delays and design backtracking, but collectively the various teams hung together and eventually worked the many problems out. Joe's actions, once the pressure to deliver subsided, seemingly made no sense. By the mid 1960s Joe had left Hallicrafters, returning to his home of Walnut Grove, Georgia and later working for nearly five years at the Lockheed-Georgia Corporation.

Always wanting to be his own boss, in 1972 Joe formed his own consulting and contract manufacturing company, Breco. Breco was involved in a host of product design and development activities for outside technology and marketing firms. One Breco product was a device to allow homeowners to monitor their electric utility consumption. Another was a series of devices to monitor pollutants emitted from incinerators. But the one that Joe credited with sinking Breco into bankruptcy was the development of clone computer devices for an overseas operation. The "operation" seemingly evaporated, and left Breco holding the bag for many thousands of dollars of unusable inventory. This, coupled with a nationwide recession in 1974–1976, spelled disaster for Breco.

Personal bankruptcy then left the Batchelors with no home or business. Fortunately, a childhood friend was able to purchase some of Joe's equipment and supplies from auction and relocated the family into an old schoolhouse. The schoolhouse had been purchased by that same childhood friend for investment purposes, but now it was reconfigured as a home and lab for a very dear friend, Joe Batchelor.

The Batchelors resided there until late 1999. Doing so allowed Joe time and resources to investigate a number of technical phenomena that he and Wes had observed while exploring wideband balanced modulators and alternative methods for single sideband. Nestled in the schoolhouse, Joe was able to spend more and more time pursuing his dreams. Had the two men remained intent on jointly stewarding new ideas and technology, who's to say how amateur radio might have benefited?

Joe Batchelor's schoolhouse lab

Chapter 18: Planned CE Products

1961 was fast shaping up to be an exciting year for Central Electronics. 100V transmitter sales were off the charts in 1960 and the early part of 1961, but Wes had big plans for its groundbreaking transmitter. As the company gained experience in building these complex transmitters, ideas for improvement bubbled up. The first thoughts were given toward streamlining the rig's assembly. The idea of chassis modules, while at first promising, made assembly of the 100V more time consuming and complex than needed.

The many wiring harness connectors became troubleshooting bottlenecks, and "ghost" problems would appear. The test team called them ghosts because most problems could be resolved by simply reconnecting suspected plugs. With the release by Amperex of improved frame-grid pentodes, the first and second mixer stages were redesigned. The elimination of plugs, the mixer tube replacements and conversion of the 100V power supply from high-vacuum tube rectifiers to the more modern solid state drove a decision to the give the upgraded radio a new name: the 200V.

The 200V went into production in April 1961, with its first and only run amounting to 500 units. Other products had been delayed due to the amount of time and energy spent getting the 100V to yield; the two most important ones were the 2500L linear amplifier and the 100R receiver, which was designed for the 100V/200V transmitters.

200V Transmitter

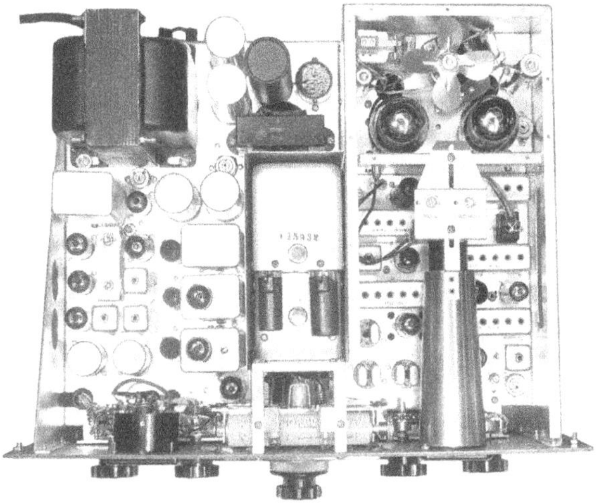

200V Transmitter interior

2500L Broadband Amplifier

Wes Schum and two lab assistants from Zenith tackled the 2500L project. The work was split into two phases, power supply and RF deck. Since the amplifier was to have an input power rating of 2500 watts (suitable for commercial use), due to size and weight of the various components, a floor-mount packaging design was favored. Separate power supply and amplifier test beds were configured, to match the two-pronged development program.

The power supply test bed was an interesting one. The plate voltage would be 2,500 volts under load and highly filtered by a choke plus a 45uF capacitor assembly. The filter capacitor would be a mylar-oil type, like that used in the 600L amplifier. A unique wrinkle engineered by Wes was the addition of a dual-purpose magnetic amplifier/filter choke. The magnetic amplifier part of the choke would dynamically vary the 240-volt plate transformer's primary, and work to stabilize plate voltage under varying load conditions.

Numerous dynamic load tests were run on the power supply test bed, and the results were deemed viable. Meanwhile, an audition of power tubes was underway, with the criteria being highest linearity/lowest intermodulation distortion. The 4CX1000, 4CX1500 and PL-172 tubes were tested, but the best candidate of all was an engineering sample provided by, of course, Amperex.

This new Amperex tube was a massive glass tetrode of a size like an Eimac 3-1000Z, but included a graphite plate, precision-aligned grids, and a heavier glass envelope. This prototype tube had the advantage of requiring axial cooling in lieu of forced air cooling. Bench tests confirmed linearity in the same class as the 4CX1500. This tube was well suited for single sideband service...plus it looked beautiful when powered up! It would have put on quite the show as the planned 2500L would have a tube viewing window.

Wes and his team had completed one 20-meter Batchelor broadband coupler and was able to produce 1750 watts output throughout the designed 1MHz passband. Yet Zenith had added product planning tasks that required Schum's full attention; therefore, work on the 2500L was suspended—temporarily, it was thought.

Ivanhoe Novice Transmitter

The FCC had created a new license class for the amateur radio service geared toward beginners. It was called the Novice Class, and was intended as a stepping stone to build the ranks of licensed ham operators. The Novice license was one-year, non-renewable one intended to introduce ham radio to newcomers. Licensees had to pass a 5 word-per-minute code test, followed by an elementary theory examination. Novice transmitters were to be crystal-controlled, continuous wave (CW) and limited to 75 watts input power.

For manufacturers, this represented a new untapped market segment. For some experienced ham operators and those in the radio industry, any accommodation made to support this new group was far less enthusiastic. Why? Who knows? But it was the wrong position to take. Amateur radio needed increased numbers to justify the valuable radio spectrum it was allowed or risk spectrum cuts, at best.

Zenith's management team, and Wes Schum, viewed the Novice Class as an opportunity to build new sales and expand good will. In June, Joe Batchelor and engineering assistant Robert Redfield were tasked with developing Central's Novice rig lineup. Joe was angered that this Novice project took away precious resources needed to finish the 2500L Linear Amplifier and the "Hot-Rod" mid-tier receiver development projects. Joe's Hot-Rod receiver, as it was code-named, was to fit underneath Central's 100R receiver, then being developed by the Zenith Military Electronics group.

Since Zenith had suggested Joe look for greener pastures, this unwanted Novice transmitter assignment made his decision an easy one. Joe immediately resigned and moved on to Hallicrafters, while Redfield was elevated to Joe's vacated engineering manager position.

By July 1st Bob Redfield had the new project moving at a breakneck pace, with the functional framework for the new Novice transmitter established. It should meet the following criteria:

1. A minimum of 75 watts input;
2. Provisions for an accessory modulator to be mounted inside the main equipment box;
3. 80–10 meters, with output circuit to match 25–500 ohms;
4. Should drive to full input from currently available VFOs;
5. Grid-blocked keying with wave shaping for minimal key clicks;
6. Meter calibrated in watts input and illuminate the meter in lieu of a panel light;

7. TVI filtered because of Class C operation;
8. The combined transmitter and modulator retail price should not exceed $89.95 for the kit, and $109.95 for the wired unit.

What's unusual about this Novice rig was not so much the technology, but Central's use of an outside and highly respected industrial design firm to handle the packaging aspects of the transmitter. Melvin Boldt and Associates was established in 1952, but by 1960 was a product packaging powerhouse in Chicago. Boldt's quality and styling influence is seen in all Zenith radios and television of the 1950s and until Zenith insourced its design efforts in the 1980s. The mock-up photograph of the rig tells the story; it looked nothing like anything previously produced by Central Electronics and was more like the new line of hi-fi component devices contemplated by Zenith.

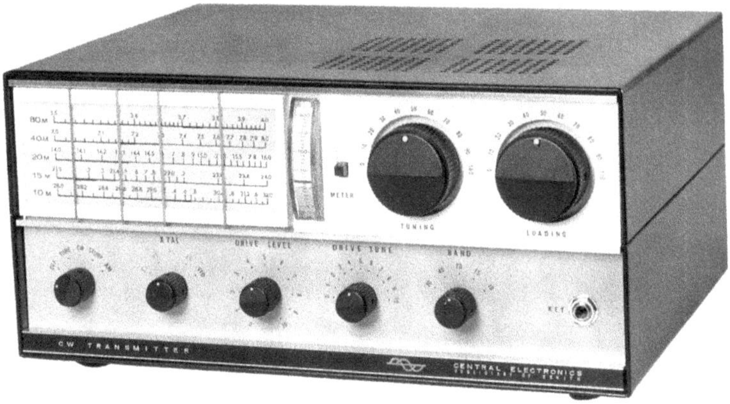

CE Ivanhoe Novice Transmitter prototype

Central had intended to construct a total of six working evaluation sets, once the project migrated out of the prototype stage. Redfield, along with Herb Saxon, Nick Fishik, and others went to work on two prototypes that were to look as close as possible to that being designed in parallel by the outside Boldt team.

By late August, the first prototype was constructed and code-named *Ivanhoe.* Component parts selection and costing was developed for Ivanhoe over the Summer of 1961, while Bob and his crew steadily worked to resolve circuit design nits. Prototype number one did not contain the AM modulator, as that was being designed in a separate but parallel path, with the aim to be eventually integrated within the prototype.

Bob's prototype was designed for the Novice Class operator having near-zero experience in radio. It had both AM (screen modulation) and CW and covered the 80- to10- meter bands. Its maximum power input was 90 watts for General Class operators and a reduced 75 watts for Novices, using a single 6146 final amplifier. The set allowed for four crystals and a VFO input. A two-stage meter was provided to measure both final grid and plate current. The rig's output Pi network was principally designed to a 50-ohm target and an optional antenna tuner would be available for balanced and unbalanced antennas.

The plan was to have Ivanhoe fully completed and ready to be marketed by March 30th, 1962; by late December 1961, that goal was clearly within easy reach. With the abrupt shutdown of Central Electronics, the Novice rig was shelved by Zenith...except for the Ivanhoe prototype, which was saved by Redfield and used by his newly licensed Novice son, as designed.

Citizen Band Equipment

The domain of post-war commercial two-way radio services was one geared to public safety, local government, and critical infrastructure operations. The public likewise desired access to low-powered, localized radio communications equipment for business use. Understanding the need and the numbers of likely users of a Citizens Band Radio Service, the FCC reallocated the former amateur 11 meter band for that use and on September 11, 1958, applications for licensing on this swath of 27MHz spectrum commenced.

Within one year, over 100,000 no-test citizens band licenses had been issued by the FCC and a steady new application rate of 8,000 per month was reached. CB instantly became a hot new market for radio equipment, and Central Electronics wanted its share of the pie. Problems in completing the 100V and later 200V rollouts had delayed Central's entry, but a principal delay was that Joe Batchelor fiercely resisted all thoughts of entry into the CB market. Joe was a ham radio purist, with little time or patience for either the Novice market or CB. In time, his initial resistance to CB was overcome and plans were coming together for Zenith to enter that lucrative market in 1962, and hopefully to build up its subsidiary's balance sheet.

Central's Len Truesdell was assigned to conduct research on the CB market and develop a breadboarded engineering prototype for management's consideration. First, Truesdell conducted a detailed survey of on-market CB radios to assess features and customer acceptance. He targeted Eico, Globe, EF Johnson, RCA, Regency, and Gonset in his studies, as these were market leaders at that time. A good number of newcomers were entering the field, but due to thin track records, poor distribution, and weak product support, the rate of new entries versus dropouts was nearly equal.

Zenith, of course had superior name recognition due to its long time, quality-based association with home entertainment equipment, including radios, televisions, hearing aids, and the newly-released audio equipment. Central could develop base and mobile CB transceivers with changeable front covers so that they could be marketed as either Central Electronics or Zenith products. The radios would be crystal controlled, limited to 5 watts, and use the Batchelor broadband coupler. By so doing, the units would be factory-tested/ready to operate once unpacked, which would eliminate the owner having to retain an FCC-licensed installation technician. A no-tune CB Radio would allow Zenith/Central to leapfrog its competition.

Central's plan was to go a step further and supply their base station radio as a complete package with a pre-tuned ground-plane antenna, and pre-assembled coaxial cables that could be ordered in 50, 75, and 100ft lengths. Sold as a complete, ready to go package, the owner or a Zenith TV repairman could install a system quickly and at low cost. Initial sales of 12,000 units in the first six months of distribution were projected, with annual sales in the order of 18,000 likely.

Two CB base station engineering prototypes were completed, with packaging under development by Melvin Boldt and Associates: the same firm that developed packaging for the Ivanhoe Novice rig. Development of a companion mobile CB unit was just weeks behind the base station. In hindsight, if the CB program had been initiated in 1959, with a delivery launch in January 1960, the volume and profitability yielded by this one product line would have delayed Zenith's exit from the amateur radio market for several years.

100R Deluxe Receiver

Now, this is a terribly sad story. Once the 100V prototype was completed in 1957, Joe and Wes immediately began work on a matching receiver, to be named 100R. Yet, complications the company faced—as caused by delayed payments by dealers, and eventual market saturation for the 10B/20A exciters—meant production of the 100V and development of its 100R receiver had to be delayed until a buyer of the business could be found.

By the end of 1957, the new 100R receiver had moved from a set of breadboard fixtures to a point where its final, detailed performance and feature specifications could be fully defined. It was to have identical frequency coverage and appearance as that of the 100V transmitter. By operating a VFO function switch on the receiver's front panel, it would be possible to change from normal, separate operation to have the system transceive on either the 100V or 100R VFO—or even transpose between the two. In 1957, *nobody* was doing that.

The receiver would contain a dual RF amplifier having remote cutoff tubes. This stage would include broadband grid/plate couplers to eliminate preselector tuning. The output of the RF amplifier would feed a bifilar compressor that would serve as an adaptive attenuator and fast AVC. The purpose of the compressor would be to protect the first mixer stage from excessively strong signals.

The principal design philosophy for this receiver was one of reduced intermodulation between sidebands. To accomplish this, Central had developed a new mixer stage that made possible intermodulation suppression of 60dB for signals spaced 1kHz apart. The receiver would be a double-conversion type, with 8MHz and 455kHz intermediate frequencies. It would employ newly released ceramic filters available from Radio Industries, Inc. The filter bandwidths would be 8kHz for AM, 3kHz and 2kHz for sideband, and 300Hz for CW.

The receiver's signal strength meter would be calibrated in microvolts, dB, and S-units. The AVC system would allow for panel-adjustable release time. An automatic T-notch would be provided that could be enabled to eliminate unstable heterodynes. If more than one heterodyne appeared in the receiver's passband, it would automatically eliminate the strongest one.

The receiver's audio system was to consist of a pair of 6BQ5 high linearity tubes as an output stage with two inverse feedback loops to further resolve distortion. An optional panoramic adapter module would be available at extra cost to be installed inside the 100R cabinet. The adapter's cathode ray tube would be the same appearance and style as that used in the 100V transmitter.

Once the 100V was finally under production in 1959, work resumed on the companion receiver. But important product launch timing had been lost while dealing with cash flow problems and becoming fully integrated within Zenith's operation. By then, everyone at Central Electronics was running at full speed, trying to recover lost ground in the marketplace. Sensing that Central's engineering staff was stretched, coupled with Zenith's interest in entering the military communications market the new ownership decided to reassign the 100R project to Zenith's defense engineering section.

That move did not sit well with either Batchelor or Schum.

Both argued, unsuccessfully, that moving the project onto an ice-cold group having little experience with amateur single sideband—or any sideband—would be a time-wasting mistake. It turned out they were right and Zenith wrong, but the owner ultimately calls the shots; this was one our home team lost.

At that time, Zenith's defense engineering section was managed by Ed Passow, a highly experienced radio engineer and long-time Zenith employee. The specific group tasked with the 100R project was itself managed by Bill Van Slyck, who was heavily involved with proximity VT fuse development during the war years. The project's lead radio engineer was James (Jim) Clark, a former design engineer at Hallicrafters.

Clark started his work in April 1959 and prepared a series of progress reports, initially in one-month intervals. April's work involved performance measurements on the competition's Drake 1A and Collins 51J-3 receivers. In addition, he reviewed the past work and circuitry breadboards as previously completed by Schum and Batchelor. The first cut Clark made in the original design was the elimination of the ceramic filters, as those would have cost $13 more than a comparable LC type filter. This resulted in a triple-conversion design with a last IF of 50kHz to accommodate the LC filter network—which increased design complexity.

Next, Clark dumped the broadband front-end design for a more traditional tuned preselector one. What he didn't appreciate was the added mechanical and electrical complexity this change introduced, since he now intended for the preselector to automatically track the VFO's tuning. Tracking of this type would have been unnecessary with the Schum/Batchelor broadband concept. The resultant gear train from Clark's design change made tuning "heavy" in the eventual prototype unit and was not warmly received by either Joe or Wes. These Zenith guys were making Central's thoroughbred receiver a more pedestrian one.

Clark's group "grafted" Batchelor's bifilar compressor, as a test case, into a Drake 1A receiver and measured an impressive 14dB intermodulation improvement. Thankfully, that meant the bifilar compressor escaped the Zenith design guillotine.

By June 1st, Zenith had completed further competitive evaluations of National NC-303 and Hammarlund HQ-170 receivers. The team had conducted tests on variable silicon capacitors (Vari-Caps) as a means of electronically tuning the frontend preselector via DC voltage in lieu of mechanical means. In the electronic scheme, the receiver's VFO would be linked to a potentiometer that would apply a tracking voltage proportional to tuned frequency to the Vari-Cap diodes. The diodes were to operate with high impressed voltages, scaled 20 to 100 volts, to circumvent diode generation of intermodulation distortion. In the end, this electronically tuned scheme was abandoned, as performance results were disappointing.

The July 1st report from Clark showed continued forward progress. Comparative performance measurements were by then completed on the Collins 75S-1 receiver. The new receiver's front panel layout was finalized, and a viable stage block diagram had been completed. Initial development of the 50kHz LC filter had hit a snag, as the first supplier of ferrite components was unsatisfactory.

A new wrinkle was added to the development mix in August. Then, consideration was given to an automatic sideband tuning scheme as a feature to enhance net operations. The concept of automatic tuning was validated by breadboard but left to be added as a downstream option. The radio's remote speaker unit was designed, and engineering samples ordered. The automatic notch system was deleted, and a manually operated T-notch included in the design.

Wiring of the first prototype receiver was nearing completion by October 1st. All stages from the 50kHz IF and back were operational, and the selectivity curves for the 50kHz filter were close to the project's design goal. The first attempt at a mechanically tuned front-end was unsatisfactory and a rework of the tracking capacitor was necessary. The mechanical gearing system was found to be too complex and added excessive frictional drag—an oft-repeated finding.

Completion of the first engineering prototype was proceeding by November 30th, and instructions given to Zenith's electrical model shop to initiate construction of six 100R pre-production receivers. In-house evaluation of the completed engineering prototype was to be completed, on air, by engineers at Zenith and Central Electronics. By January 15th (now 1960), the prototype was to undergo an in-depth material and production cost analysis. Zenith's patent officers had undertaken a search to determine prospects for gaining a patent on the receiver's novel bifilar compressor, and concluded there was a clear pathway ahead.

Soon after, the engineering team discovered receiver front end signal leakage issues that required a significant mechanical re-work of that stage's mechanical layout and wiring dress. The last modification to the bifilar compressor coil was made in late January, with performance normalized over the range of 1.5 to 30MHz, a significant achievement. The 100R engineering prototype was fully completed by March 1st.

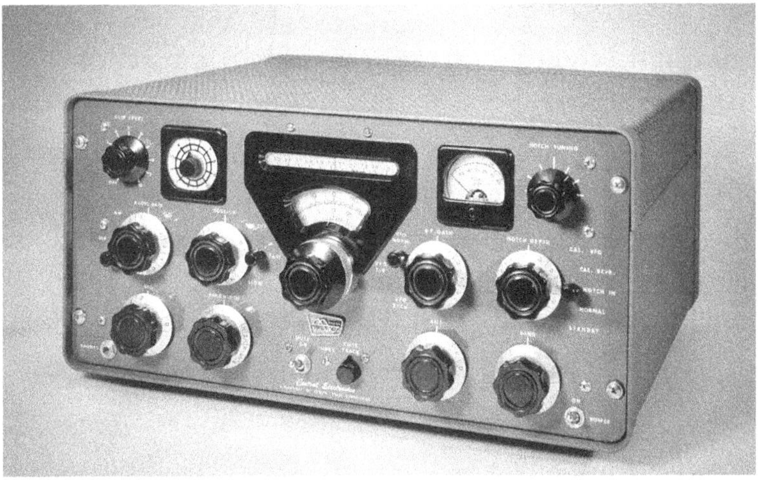

100R Receiver prototype

A cost study for the receiver was completed by May 1st, and it was bad news: the costs for construction were deemed too high. Immediate cost reduction alternatives of $50 were initially identified, but some of those changes would impact downstream reliability. One such cost-lowering strategy, for example, would have replaced ceramic switch wafers in the band switch and mode selectors to phenolic types. A redesign of the 50kHz IF filter coils could also lead to lowered cost, but likely a lowering in adjacent channel rejection performance. Making the notch filter an option could further reduce base cost. (Keep in mind that each $1 savings in manufacturing cost could translate into a $2.50 to $3.00 reduction on sales price.)

The brakes were applied to the 100R project, and nobody was happy.

Off and on, the 100R project was revisited, but the project could never be brought to a cost point that Zenith was comfortable in proceeding. Frankly, it never could cost out since Zenith was applying overhead cost percentages that were typical for its *television* production, which were wholly unrealistic for an operation of Central's size and potential production volume. To my knowledge, none of the six pre-production receivers were completed, although a few of the 100R's accessory speaker prototypes have been found. In fact, I am listening to one while writing this book!

In hindsight, Zenith's ultraconservative approach to cost versus volume was unnecessary. The 100R would then have been in the same cost category as a Collins 75A-4, but with significantly more features. Surely, if Collins could sell its 75A-4 and the hugely expensive KWS-1 transmitter (they weren't called the Gold Dust Twins for nothing), surely Zenith could sell its feature-rich 100R. Of the nearly 2,000 combined 100V/200V transmitter owners, it was probable that at least half if not more of those would have bought the matching receiver, no questions asked.

Zenith didn't understand the market, which was Batchelor's and Schum's biggest fear. Nor did Zenith have appreciation for the depth of interest Central Electronics had built for the 100R, 2500L and other products. The model for selling radio communication equipment to radio hobby enthusiasts was far different than that needed to sell television sets. When was the last time anyone asked about intermodulation rejection or adjacent channel selectivity when shopping for a TV?

Zenith just didn't get it. The net result was that no production of 100R receivers occurred before Central's deactivation in January 1962.

Fortunately, the one 100R prototype survived and was for many years owned by Bill Van Slyck, the 100R design team's manager. Then, it was paired with a 100V transmitter and used by him on 20 meters, happily chasing DX.

Wes Schum in his McClellan Lab in 1964

Chapter 19: Rebirth and Schum Electronics

Once the shock of being suddenly unemployed wore off, Wes had no time for self-pity. He had a family to support: a wife, mother-in-law, four kids, and a dog. Zenith had no interest in continuing to build language lab equipment for the Jay L. Warren Company, so Wes was able to carry that part of the business away.

But he had no manufacturing facility. Now what?

By then, the Schums were living next door to the Edgebrook Woods Forest Preserve in Chicago. Today, it is over 138 acres of pristine forest, teaming with wildlife, and an unusual oddity in the Windy City. The Schums' residence at 6223 North McClellan had a wonderful view of the Preserve, fully green during the spring and summer and blanketed in snow during the fall and winter months. Deer and other small animals made the area special.

When Wes and Marge bought the home and adjoining property in the mid-1950s, it needed substantial renovation and the neighborhood was truly middle class. But as the economy of Chicago boomed, many of the area's well-to-do were gradually attracted to the neighborhood, moved in, and became the Schums' neighbors. By the 1980s, the list included high profile lawyers, judges, and even a US Senator.

The Schums' residence at 6223 North McClellan Street

Little did anyone suspect that Wes Schum had single-handedly created an electronics manufacturing business in his downstairs basement. Piece by piece, he assembled work benches, wire harness layout tables, parts storage shelving, coil winding stations, and metal working gear, including brakes, shears, a riveting machine, and even a punch press. He had also configured a homebrewed paint booth and printed circuit board layout and etching station.

In the basement business called Schum Electronics, Wes had created a vertically integrated manufacturing haven. Raw materials came in, cabinets and chassis were formed, circuit boards were made, cabinets painted, completed equipment tested and packaged for shipment, and nobody else knew anything about it! There was no sign outside; he had only word of mouth advertising. Even the family was instructed to answer the telephone a certain way: "Schum..." No matter if friends called, the answer was the same. Marge and her mother, Lillian, who lived with the family at this time, were responsible for making the wire harnesses. And the assembly line would continue to grow as each daughter turned 13 and was taught how to solder. It had truly become a family affair! It was also during this time that Marge was inspired to get her amateur radio license. She became K9EMP which she jokingly referred to as "Eat More Possum."

Having the business set-up within the confines of his own home also gave Schum an advantage that he could not benefit from if his workshop was located elsewhere. Wes had a very unique gift in that design ideas would often come to him in his sleep. He could frequently be found at his drawing board in the wee hours of the night after an idea or solution to a problem had awakened him. When he was actually able to apply the "dream state" thoughts to his work the next morning, he found that they worked more often than not so it was worth the trip from his bed to the basement. There were even times where he would fall asleep while talking to a work colleague and still be able to provide viable answers to their questions. Wes' brain was truly wired for electronics!

The creation of this subterranean labyrinth of design and construction came together with extreme urgency. Wes had firmly decided to never again get in a position where he was employed by others who didn't share his vision or commitment to succeed. In fact, others did approach Wes once word came of Central's demise, the most notable being Mr. Edgar Johnson, owner of the E.F. Johnson Company.

The E. F. Johnson Company manufactured electronic components such as tube sockets, variable capacitors, and other parts used by manufactures of all types. In the amateur radio circles, the company built a line of AM and CW transmitters that were known for their reliability and quality. Important product names such as Ranger, Valiant, and Thunderbolt continue to be sought units by collectors of vintage radio equipment. Johnson had an early attempt at fielding a single sideband rig, Pacemaker, but it was in all respects an engineering disaster and as Wes put it, gave the phasing method of sideband generation a bad name.

Johnson offered Wes an unbelievable opportunity to join their Waseca based operation, and at a salary more than twice what Wes had made at Zenith. The answer was a swift "Thanks, but no." Wes Schum had made up his mind to strike out on his own, with no partners other than Marge Schum.

At this point in time the family found itself able to do quite a bit of traveling. Imagine Wes, Marge, Grandma Lillie and all four girls riding across the USA in a station wagon for a month at a time. When the letters "CQCQ" were spoken into the mic, it was understood that Wes needed some "Ham" time and all the chatter would immediately cease. On one of the trips out "West" Wes made contact with a fellow operator who subsequently invited him to his home in Arizona. Wes very excitedly accepted the invitation and gave the girls a stern warning to behave themselves where they were going to visit. Once there, they were all on good behavior until the older two girls followed the adults into the ham shack. The two younger ones lagged behind because they had found something very interesting to them. It was a small, hinged door cut into a door leading to the backyard.

Having never seen a curiosity like this before, they decided to check it out. After multiple trips through the door and an increase in the laughter volume, the adults returned to check out the ruckus. All of a sudden the older of the two mischief makers felt a hand grab onto the back of her pants as she was yanked back into the kitchen. Next came the booming words from Wes, "And just what do you think you are doing? That door is for dogs, not little girls!" Needless to say, the two guilty daughters spent the remainder of the visit on the couch.

There was a long lecture once back in the car as to how to behave when visiting the home of others, especially that of the U.S. Senator and past presidential candidate, Barry Goldwater.

By the Summer of 1962, Schum Electronics was well underway. It had resumed work for the Jay L. Warren Company and had developed a new language lab system called Walk-Away. This design consisted of a multi-channel turntable/speech source and fully transistorized wearable units for students. The system utilized a magnetic loop system that was installed along the perimeter of a language lab classroom, allowing the teacher's signal to be received by class students.

The entire system, inclusive of the auditory training unit as well as the student's portable set, was designed and constructed by Schum. Wes found a ready group of assembly technicians from the nearby Teletype Corporation factory in Skokie, IL, as well as people who worked at Motorola but were open to moonlighting for Schum.

In addition to this work, Schum was successful in gaining a contract to build stereo FM test sets for Zenith Radio. The home audio market by then was expanding, and Zenith was selling home entertainment centers by the train car loads. Its constellation of authorized Zenith services stations were clamoring for the test equipment necessary to service those units. Zenith had electrically designed the needed test gear but needed a contractor to build a run of 1,500 sets.

That was right up Schum's alley. Once a contract was in place, his crew of workers was temporarily expanded using ham radio pals and their XYLs (wives) to accommodate the run's delivery schedule. And so it went; Wes Schum had not only recovered from the shock of losing Central Electronics, he was hot on the trail of new ideas and opportunities as well.

Just as the work with Zenith was winding down, a new opportunity presented itself. One of his former Central Electronics dealers who worked for Western Electric told Wes about a manufacturing problem they were facing. The Bell System was beginning to allow what it termed "foreign" connections to its wired network; this was not fully a voluntary move, but one brought about by the FCC. The connection interfaces made by outside firms had to conform to a 1,500-volt network isolation spec, but Western Electric needed test sets to verify compliance. Initially they needed just 100 sets, but the need could grow to 1,500. Would Wes be interested?

Yes, he was.

Within 30 days, a prototype was developed for Western Electric's consideration. After a week, the first order was placed. That was filled in 60 days. Other orders followed, and sure enough, they amounted to 1,500 units. Keep in mind, every one of those test sets was built in the Schum basement operation!

Next came a call from the Audio Development Company, ADC. They had a yield problem with telephone jackfields that were failing quality control (QC) tests. For some reason, in a jackfield containing 48 individual jacks, occasionally a few were found to have electrical short circuits, rendering the whole assembly unusable. Could Schum see if ADC's test process was wrong? The problem, he found, wasn't with the test process, but the mechanical assembly of the jacks themselves. When jack parts were being assembled, tiny flakes of conductive steel or copper were finding their way into the works and causing short circuits. Wes figured if he could impart enough electrical energy in a pulse, he could maybe evaporate the minute shorting particles and recover usable jackfields.

Schum built two evaluation models of his subsequently designed HVBU-1 Burn Unit, and it worked to perfection. In just a week's worth of evaluation testing, ADC had repaired 70% of the jackfields it had previously written off as junk. Soon, word of this neat device spread back to Western Electric, where other HVBU-1s were pressed into service and used to eliminate "whiskers" on printed circuit boards. A whisker was a small bit of copper that had not been full etched away in the board manufacturing process and then caused short circuits between traces. The Schum HVBU turned out to be the answer. When applied to Western Electric's growing pile of failed, unpopulated circuit boards, most all could be repaired by simply burning away the errant whisker.

And so it went. First Bell Labs, then Western Electric, Teletype Corporation, Lenkurt, and even Motorola began asking Schum to design other high voltage test sets for their production line needs. These were manufactured by Schum in relatively low numbers, orders of twenty to fifty at a time. But due to their unique features and low production volume, which fit perfectly with Schum's basement operation, the company's profit margin was high; Wes soon found himself looking for some R&R. The answer was fox hunting, and not the kind that involved a red, furry animal. His local Chicago ham group had come up with a fun version of hide-and-seek. The operator designated as the fox would find a hiding place, from which he would broadcast "HO HO HO, this is the fox;" the winner of the game was the first operator to find him. This could take quite a while as it encompassed not only the entire city, but the outlying areas as well. It usually went smoothly, with the fox being located and the evening ending in Chicago-style deep-dish pizza at a favorite restaurant. There were a few exceptions, however; some hunts didn't end so well.

One in particular came about when the fox decided to hide in an alley dumpster in the city. He apparently scared a local resident who promptly called the police. Upon their arrival, the officers found him sitting in the dumpster with a "crazy electronic device," in the middle of broadcasting the "HO HO HO, this is the fox" message. After some intense questioning and a stiff warning the ham was free to go, and the eventual meet up at the local restaurant was more animated than usual!

The Explorer line of test sets were designed to accommodate one specific test, although voltage levels and leakage current limits were field settable by the owner. A total of five Explorer models were developed, the last of those shipped to ADC's operation in Mexico and Teletype's second factory in Little Rock, Arkansas. The most interesting of the Schum test sets were the Omni series.

The Omni test set was designed to provide for two sequential high voltage tests, each of which had fully customizable test parameters. The test setup's various controls were grouped behind two front doors, ar acknowledgment to Schum's famous 100V and 200V transmitters. I suppose if there would have ever been a resumption of ham radio products from Schum Electronics, there is no doubt those would also have that Omni look.

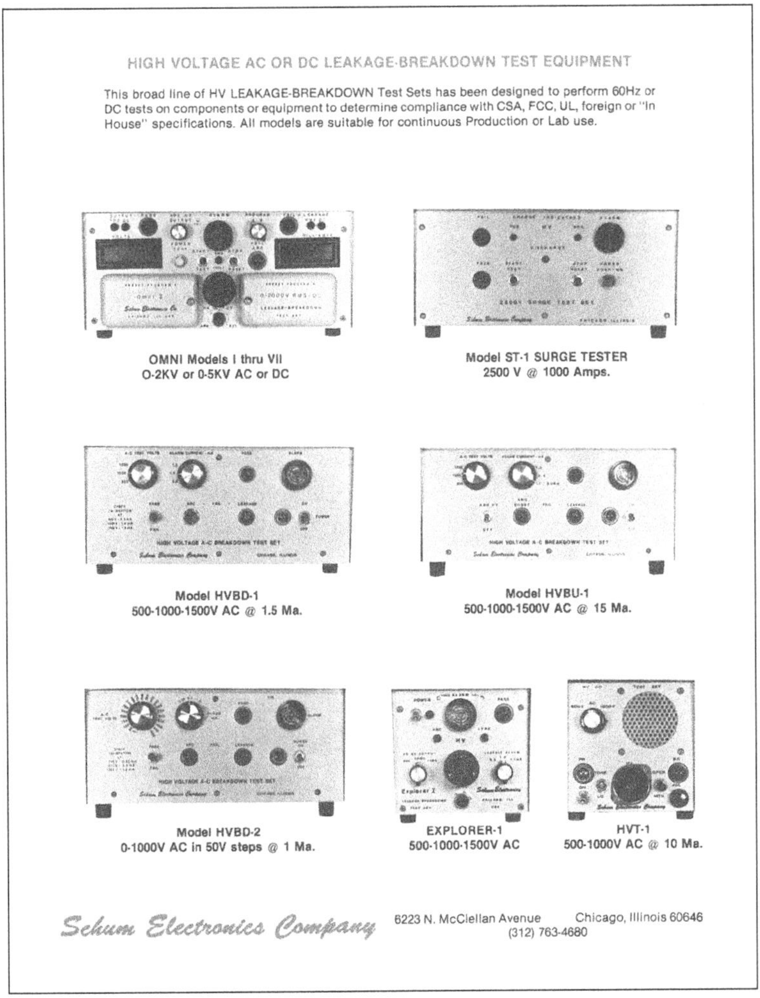

Meanwhile, the design and production of new systems for the Jay L Warren Company continued. Successive models, first the T-3 and later the T-4, were developed. The magnetic loop concept gave way to non-licensed FCC Part 15 complaint channelized radio systems and the ability for students to individually talk back to their teachers, all designed by Schum Electronics. Wes continued to make equipment and replacement parts for the Warren systems until the early 1980s, over thirty-five years after those important first tests at the Ephpheta School.

Warren T-2 made by Central Electronics

Warren Auditory Training Unit

MODEL T-3 S/S with Lavalliere Microphone **$675.00** F.O.B. CHICAGO Shipping Wt. 32 lbs.

THE STORY OF GATED COMPRESSION

The introduction of WARREN auditory training equipment in 1948 with gated compression opened a new window of hope for the aurally-handicapped child. The patented gated compression system automatically maintains the volume output at a pre-determined level. Weak sounds are increased and loud sounds are compressed. The result is a smooth even flow of sound volume virtually free of distortion. The teachers can work with normal voice levels, yet insure that the student receives full sound volume. The unique gated compression circuit provides rapid control of sound level peaks reducing them to predetermined levels for the student. The system has none of the delayed action of ordinary automatic volume control systems.

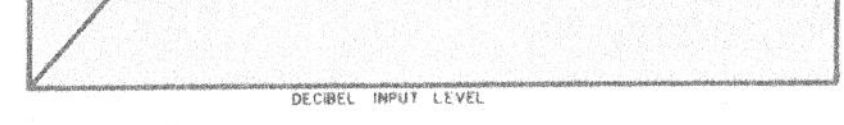

The above graph shows the superiority of Gated Compression

CUSTOM BUILT—PROFESSIONAL NEW MODEL T-3 S/S

The Jay L. Warren, Inc. CUSTOM BUILT, Professional Model T-3 Auditory Training Unit is designed in the tradition of superior quality and engineering, with the assistance and accumulated recommendations of prominent educators of the deaf, which has made WARREN the leader in the field for over twenty (20) years.

Using the "GATED COMPRESSION" (patented #2,659,777) circuit in a fully transistorized amplifier, the Model T-3 S/S is completely compatible with existing WARREN equipment and accessories now in use—thus providing new standards of flexibility, performance and reliability.

The WARREN T-3 S/S GATED COMPRESSION Auditory Training Unit has full provisions for individual teacher/student instruction. Input channels for the teacher's microphone with supplementary phonograph and magnetic tape input permit wide range of teaching techniques. The student is provided with a directly controlled gated compression output.

The WARREN T-3 S/S GATED COMPRESSION Auditory Training Unit can provide group instruction through calibrated, binaural outlet boxes or with 8 separate channels through the crystal controlled WARREN Channelator system to group students with WALK-AWAY receiving units. Each student is provided with binaurally controlled sound levels and is free to move and participate in the teaching program.

Warren T-3 made by Schum Elecrtronics

Warren T-4

Schum's business continued to do well throughout the late 1970s and early 1980s, but troubling signs were appearing. Congress fell asleep and let America's manufacturing infrastructure slip away to foreign competitors. Some of the worst of those atrocities involved the senseless decimation of the domestic entertainment electronics industry. One by one, important names in radio and television manufacturing were forced to close up shop, victims of unfair trade practices and the dumping of foreign equipment into the US—at times below actual manufacturing costs. As the domestic electronics industry dried up, so too did the domestic suppliers of important electronic components.

The sole purpose of foreign dumping—then and now—is to drive American manufacturers out of business. Congress let it happen. We were defeated without a single shot fired.

It didn't stop with home electronics. Even telephones and other home appliances were being made offshore. With each chip from America's manufacturing base, some of Schum's business eroded as well. Schum's equipment was used principally by manufacturers; if those clients were no longer in the manufacturing business, Schum was no longer needed.

The wave of outward manufacturing migration wasn't immediate, fortunately. At first some manufacturers moved operations to Mexico in search of cheaper labor to maintain some competitive edge over the Fast East. Zenith, ADC, and Motorola's industrial lighting division went that route, and all needed new Schum tests sets for newly established production lines. The Far East's response was to simply cut their selling prices even more. In short, it became a battle that domestic manufacturers could never win.

While the timing and ultimately the consequences of outsourcing and dismantling domestic manufacturing wasn't right fiscally or socially for America, it turned out okay for Wes Schum. Approaching 70 years of age in 1991, he made the decision to phase out of his testing equipment business and retire to Tennessee. It was there that he entered yet another new adventure in life with Marge, Roy Sherman (long-time friend/business associate/housemate), daughter Diane and her family. He helped build a homestead, where he enjoyed spending time with family and friends that is still a gathering place for everyone to this day.

During this part of his life, Wes continued to enjoy his time on the air with ham radio, but had noticed his hearing was increasingly giving him trouble. He decided, in typical Wes form, that he didn't need any of those "horrible new hearing aids that had to go inside your ears and hurt like hell," but would instead manufacture something of his own. He worked with an old Radio Shack radio and some earbuds, and voila, he had a hearing aid that he could carry around in his front shirt pocket, and it didn't hurt his ears at all. Everyone thought he was really cool, listening to tunes or a ball game, which made his day! Eventually, when the old radio unit bit the dust, he succumbed and bought a set of those new hearing aids that "Weren't so bad after all."

Wes had time to rediscover his love of gardening and to fish on the shores of his farm pond with his grandkids, as he had once done long ago on lake and river shores as a lad with his dad. He was also able to renew his love of animals through his grandchildren's numerous farm pets. He made lifelong friends of his two favorites: McMann the rooster, and Chunk, a 35-pound Toulouse goose. They followed him everywhere he went, and when Wes went indoors, they would faithfully wait for his return, crowing, honking, or tapping on his basement workshop window (which still has the crack they made in it to this day). Yes, retirement for Wes was indeed good!

Wes relaxing in retirement with his feathered friend

By now you may be wondering how I got to know Wes. Actually, that began in 1967. I had become a freshman at Jesuit High School in New Orleans but was already a ham two years earlier. The ham bug had bitten hard, and I was devouring anything in print about Radio. My hangout was at our neighbor's garage-based radio/tv repair shop. There I became his "autonomous" tube tester!

At Jesuit, we had a ham radio club, something that was quite common among high schools throughout the USA then; remember, there was no Internet! I first learned of Central Electronics as a freshman student in 1967. The school's radio club, WA5SCH, was moderated by a Jesuit priest, Fr. Milton Reich, who owned a 10A, a homebrewed amplifier, and a Collins 75A-1/Model A slicer rig. Fr. Reich was no longer active, but he allowed us to use his gear. And did we ever use it! A good many of those guys became EEs and started businesses in various technical disciplines.

The club's 10A had only 80 meter and 40M meter coils, and with the sunspot cycle in high gear, club members were eager for action on 20 meters. What to do but write to Zenith and get info on how to make coils sets for the other bands? Can you believe I received a handwritten response from Karl Hassel, who was a co-founder of Zenith? It was he who directed me to this fellow Wes Schum, and the start of a life-long friendship.

By the time college came around, I was at Tulane University's Electrical Engineering Department and keen as anything for a new project. Of course, I knew about the 100V transmitter, but the only local ham who had one guarded it like a hawk. So, I started calling Wes Schum, first to get a 100V instruction manual and then to pester him with questions. At the time, he was loaded up with Warren redesign work and so most of my calls were intercepted by Dillard Carr, one of the technicians he had recruited from Central Electronics.

Eventually I found a nice 100V for sale, scooped it up, and started dissecting it. I soon discovered that its Batchelor output couplers looked nothing like the patent, which is when I discovered the Heuer

Coupler. Drat, I had to buy another set to lay eyes on the Batchelor broadband crown jewels!

Now, of course, the challenge was to make one myself. That's what eventually lead to me travelling to Chicago and finally meeting Wes Schum.

I did as much research as I could about broadband matching networks of this type and found *nothing*. It was as if when Central Electronics was shut down, everything about the broadband coupler disappeared from the face of the Earth. So, I started working it out, one misstep at a time. A good ham pal of mine, Ron Scalise WA5ZFP was likewise interested, so we buddied up to figure it out. He conjured up some sweep test gear, and I designed a test fixture. Together, we built a power amplifier test bed, first with a pair of Eimac 4CX800s tubes, and later a single 8877.

Little by little, secrets were unlocked. I'd telephone Wes, who would listen intently to our progress and might make a suggestion when a snag was hit. It was only when we stumbled that he offered clues; we had to put up a lot of sweat equity first! Eventually we had our 8877 test fixture delivering a steady 1750 watts on 20 meters.

That's when I headed up to Chicago. It was the middle of January 1984, and an unbelievably cold day. When I got off the plane, it was -10 degrees, ice everywhere, and the wind off Lake Michigan was over 20 miles per hour. I was dressed like a true southerner, in a sweater with a topcoat, and freezing to death. To make matters more interesting, I had never driven in ice or snow. Wintry weather is not something that happens frequently in New Orleans.

As I carefully and ever so slowly drove (crept) up McClellan Avenue toward the Schum home, not only was the snow as white, smooth and thick as in the movie *It's a Wonderful Life*, there were deer in his front yard!

How can that be, in the middle of Chicago?! I remember thinking.

Wes opened the door, somewhat in shock seeing my less than adequate cold weather protection, and rushed me in. That was the start of my Chicago visits, every four months for a week at a time, always scheduled to coincide with a local hamfest.

During those weeks in town, I'd help Wes build his test equipment orders and he would introduce me to his favorite excess inventory parts emporiums. We'd hit Mid-America Electronics, where I thought I had died and gone to radio parts heaven; Bristol Electronics in Antioch, Wisconsin; or Albergo Transformers, in the Italian section of the city. It seemed there was a never-ending list of surplus electronics parts houses to scope out and buy parts in the quantities needed for a small electronics' fab operation…both for his, and soon, my own.

In short, Wes took a young ham operator from New Orleans under his wing and pointed the way to my dreams of building communications products and running a successful business. Plus, I gradually drew out of him the story he kept so close, that of Central Electronics. We became as close as father and son.

Looking back, Wes Schum was a content man. His dream for amateur radio single sideband had materialized; he had become a manufacturer of a product line his life-long hobby needed. Schum's language lab equipment helped young children hear, speak, and lead more productive lives. His test equipment products allowed the Schum family to live the full American dream.

Retirement was looking good for Wes Schum, W9DYV!

Joe, Wes, and Nick circa 1997

Chapter 20: The W9DYV Radio Society

"You mean hams collect and still *operate* my radios?" In the 1980s, Wes had no idea that people were still so interested in Central Electronics and were eagerly collecting and operating 10As, 20As... everything. Why, it had been over 25 years, and so many other radios and manufacturers had come and gone. With his focus on products for Schum Electronics and a self-imposed retreat from 75–10 meters, Wes had missed the dawn of the "boatanchor restorer" era.

So, as I asked more questions about the people and product ideas at Central, and even explained that people were beginning to send radios to me to repair, Wes was genuinely surprised. Now, when we went to local hamfests, not only was he pointing out the 10As, 20As or the occasional 100V we spotted, he began striking up conversations with their owners. Soon, after sensing interest, he'd explain that those rigs were from his former company.

Now, that was something!

People weren't asking any hard questions about Central and Zenith; they were more interested in meeting the man behind the radios. Soon, Wes was giving sideband discussions again, first to the Society of Radio Operators—a long time Chicago ham radio club—and then to the Illinois chapter of the Old Timers Club. As the move to Tennessee grew closer, we'd discuss what sort of antenna farm to build, where to put the new W9DYV ham shack, and plans to refurbish his long dormant 200V/600L rig. That 200V was special: It was Central's engineering prototype, serial number 1, that traveled with him to sideband conferences in many states.

Figuring a bit more fire in his antennas might come in handy, a 3-1000Z final amplifier was conjured for the new shack, as a going away present.

When Wes first saw that big floor model amplifier, his eyes grew wide as saucers. A huge grin slowly grew on his face and a knowing look suggested visions, in his mind's eye, of that 200V sounding really, *really* big—opening up the bands! No fault in that, eh? What ham op can possibly resist a big, sexy glass final amplifier tube, especially one that pulsates between red and bright yellow on voice peaks?

That's what amateur radio is all about! Alas, folks running lightweight solid-state amplifiers that merely sit on a desk, make nary a sound, and offer no visual light show sadly don't know what they're missing. Those big vacuum tubes are the mystique of ham radio DXing.

Soon, W9DYV was in ham radio heaven back on 160 meters, finding a whole group of new radio friends throughout Tennessee, Virginia, and the Carolinas. He became a regular at the Shelby Carolina Hamfest, and others. A new lab—configured in the basement, of course—offered a fertile environment for renewed experimentation on ways to compress single sideband voice energy—something that Joe Batchelor was likewise studying in his schoolhouse lab's inner sanctum.

For those fifteen retirement years in Jonesborough, Tennessee, W9DYV was having the time of his life and enjoying ham radio once again.

Over the past twenty years, there has been a growing interest among amateur radio enthusiasts to preserve, restore, and operate early '50s vintage single sideband equipment. Collectors have gravitated to the equipment of our youth, items made by such companies as Collins,

Hallicrafters, National, EF Johnson, Heath, and Central Electronics. On-air Sunday afternoon nets such as the 20 Meter Vintage Sideband Net (14.292MHz) and the Collins Collectors Net (14.263MHz) attract many who enjoy operating these old but still relevant pieces of radio's history. Organizations such as the Antique Wireless Association hold annual meets where discussions on the history of radio's many past contributors and manufacturers are held. Contests involving the best original, restored, or homebrewed radio artifacts are admired and draw many like-minded enthusiasts.

It should come as no surprise that Central Electronics enthusiasts looked to Wes Schum's 90th birthday as an appropriate time to hold both a celebration and technical symposium to herald that milestone. First held in 2012, the annual W9DYV Symposium has become the place for sideband enthusiasts to meet, learn, and share experiences with others. Sure, the main topics center on vintage sideband manufacturers and restoration ideas, yet many enterprising amateurs have moved the needle further. At any given symposium, one might find information on how to build transceiver adapters for Central Electronic or other radios, how to homebrew tube-type rigs, or how to merge the latest Arduino and software defined radio ideas with more "elderly" ones.

Wes always enjoyed meeting old and new hams at these symposiums and was thrilled to see people finding new ways to make their on-air radio experiences more exciting.

Now it is up to the next generation of enthusiasts to draw amateur radio into new and exciting directions. All it takes is one person to make a difference. If you believe in an idea strongly enough and put your entire being into the endeavor, success can be yours and the sky the limit...as it was for Wes Schum.

Appendix I: Modulation Schemes

The two basic forms of adding intelligence onto a radio frequency signal involve instantaneously modifying either the amplitude or frequency (and hence, phase) of the host, carrier signal. Both types of modulation produce new frequencies, which combine with the carrier signal to produce a resultant waveform envelope.

Amplitude modulation causes these resultant waveforms to vary in intensity in step with the intelligence information, usually speech. In frequency modulation, the frequency of the waveform is made to vary in step with the intelligence information. In either instance, the intelligence is termed the modulating signal. They are abbreviated as AM and FM (or PM for phase modulation). Keep in mind that when a radio signal's frequency is varied, then so too is its phase, from cycle to cycle, when referenced to the unmodulated state.

Keep in mind, that when a carrier wave is amplitude modulated, its carrier frequency remains a constant. Whereas in a frequency modulated carrier wave, the carrier's amplitude remains a constant value, but its operating frequency varies in step with the modulating intelligence signal. The amount a frequency modulated carrier varies depends upon the amplitude of the information signal. The rate at which the carrier signal varies depends upon the frequency of the modulating signal.

AM can be generated at various points within a radio transmitter. The most usual way is to apply the modulating signal in series with the final amplifier's tube (transistor) plate (collector) DC supply. The output of the transmitter's carrier wave is then varied in step with the instantaneous voltage changes caused by the modulating signal. This means is termed plate (or collector) modulation.

Likewise, it is possible to amplitude modulate a transmitter's carrier wave by varying the grid bias on a RF amplifier, in step with the modulating signal—or, in the case of tetrode power tubes, the instantaneous screen grid voltage.

Each of these methods is capable of producing amplitude modulated carrier waves.

When a carrier wave is modulated by a single audio tone, two additional signals are produced. Along with the original carrier signal, there is now one signal above and below the carrier wave's frequency, and spaced by the frequency of the audio tone. So, if the radio carrier was 4MHz and the audio tone 1kHz, then the resultant AM signal would consist of the carrier wave, the carrier wave plus 1kHz, and the carrier wave minus 1kHz—or 3.999MHz, 4.000MHz, and 4.001MHz.

The bandwidth of the resultant AM signal would then be 2kHz, or twice the modulating tone. So, if the audio tone was 3kHz, then the bandwidth of the transmitted signal would be 6kHz.

Now, if the audio tones were replaced by speech energy that spanned 300Hz to 3500Hz, then two sidebands of energy would be produced above and below the carrier and the occupied bandwidth of the signal would be 7kHz. Note that the two sidebands are in fact exact replicas of the original 1kHz tone—or, in the case of the speech example, the information contained within the original 300–3500Hz base signal.

Single sideband is merely the process of eliminating the resultant carrier and one redundant sideband from an amplitude modulated signal. By so doing, it is then possible to project the same base tone or speech intelligence, but in just half the space occupied by a normal AM signal.

Appendix II: Early Correspondence

The base design of Wes Schum's Model 10A sideband exciter closely followed the principals initiated by Don Norgaard, an electrical engineer employed by the General Electric Company. Wes took the Norgaard design, as described by General Electric's Ham News, and made it far more flexible and useful to the amateur radio community. The following sets of letters document the interaction between Wes and the General Electric Company in those early, formative years of Central Electronics.

Initially the 10A was sold by word-of-mouth and Wes' full court press approach to selling Hams on the value of single sideband. Eventually, in 1952, the fledgling company had secured enough sales backlog that it could gamble on advertising in QST magazine. With that, the Model 10A exciters began flying out of Schum's West Giddings Street garage factory at a breakneck pace and the new company gained an eager and enthusiastic following.

The following set of correspondence helps frame the military's early use of singe-sideband and the back-room work that ultimately made efficient voice communications for radio amateurs a commercial reality.

GENERAL ELECTRIC
COMPANY

Research Laboratory

THE KNOLLS . . . SCHENECTADY, NEW YORK . . . TELEPHONE 4-2211

P.O. Box 1088

August 27, 1952

Mr. W. R. Schum
Central Electronics Inc.
2125 W. Giddings Street
Chicago 25, Illinois

Dear Mr. Schum:

I have looked over the circuit diagrams of the Sideband Slicer Model A and the Multiphase Exciter with great interest. Both units seem to have everything necessary for doing the job in good fashion.

Two things in the exciter caught my eye. The first was the coupling arrangement between the modulator tank circuit and the 6BA7 mixer tube. I wonder why the extra tuned circuit (L_4 and C_{21}) is interposed at this point.

The 15 MC trap associated with the mixer was apparently put in to reduce 15 MC third harmonic oscillator output when operating on the 14 MC band. The question is, how effective is this arrangement? With only 5 MC on the grids #1 and #2 it seems to me that third harmonic current can still be generated in the tube and appear in the output. I believe a more effective location would be somewhere in the plate circuit of the mixer, not necessarily a parallel trap in series with the plate, but perhaps a series trap tuned to shunt the plate at 15 MC. Perhaps you have tried this and find that it interferes too much with tracking of C_{30} and C_{36}. What I had in mind was saving a few parts and eliminating at least one tune-up adjustment too.

Anyway, the exciter does a very nice job from what I hear of them on the air. Other people comment very favorably on them too. I'm glad that you have done such a good job on the exciter in general, for this should very effectively boost the popularity of single-sideband.

As I mentioned Thursday night, I have done a great deal of work toward Villard's scheme of using multiple phase-shift networks to improve sideband rejection. This work has all been paper work aimed at possible practical applications of the method. So far, I have not discovered any arrangement that I consider worth while in view of the

GENERAL ELECTRIC

Mr. Schum -2- August 27, 1952

fact that one can realize around 40 DB with existing phase-shift networks. Basically the problem is to apply the method (or kindred ones) with the precision that balance ratios beyond 40 DB demand. It seems to me that any actual improvement is going to be had through refinement of the phase-shift networks themselves rather than in weird combinations of less perfect ones. In setting the arbitrary goal of 40 DB rejection for present practical schemes full recognition is required of the fact that amplifier and modulator distortions generally will degrade any theoretical improvement materially beyond this convenient limit. In other words, what is needed is amplifiers, modulators, and components which greatly surpass presently available ones with respect to stability and distortion. In addition, we need equipment and procedures that will tell us when we have acutally made an improvement. The law of diminishing returns is a hard one to beat. ↖ actually

I hope the enclosed treatment will be helpful to you. It may stimulate you to the extent that you will find the magic combination. To be useful, however, the magic combination has to eliminate extremely small errors of adjustment automatically. Good luck.

Very truly yours,

D. E. Norgaard

D. E. Norgaard

DEN/vjs

RESTRICTED

HEADQUARTERS
AIRWAYS AND AIR COMMUNICATIONS SERVICE
WASHINGTON 25, D. C.

AACS-D-353 28 April 1950

SUBJECT: Single Side-Band Training Program

TO: Commanding Officer
1804th AACS Group
APO 942, c/o Postmaster
Seattle, Washington

1. Information contained herein will be disseminated to all maintenance personnel.

2. The Single Side-Band Program was initiated to meet the increased world-wide postwar circuit requirements. The program calls for the installation of multi-channel Single Side-Band equipment at certain strategic locations to meet the demands of a USAF Global Communications System.

3. Planning indicated that a requirement existed for one hundred (100) specially trained Single Side-Band Mechanics. The nature and complexity of the equipment, and the priority of the program indicated that the mechanics chosen for this training should be the best available within the AACS from a standpoint of experience, ability and education, and should be proven career airmen; plus a number of skilled maintenance officers.

4. A message was subsequently dispatched from this Headquarters command-wide requesting that recommendations be forwarded from unit commanders for this training and a list was compiled by this Headquarters of personnel so recommended. On the establishment of the Single Side-Band Factory School by the Western Electric Company in New York City, students were selected from this list on a most qualified basis for attendance.

5. The second class is now in attendance and is due to graduate on or about 15 May 1950. The third class has been selected and will report to the Factory School on 1 June 1950. Classes will continue at six (6) week intervals until mid-1951; at which time it is expected that our quota of one hundred (100) mechanics will be graduated. Effective 1 June 1950, classes will be composed of twelve (12) students each.

6. Installation and project data:

a. The following circuits will comprise this Global or "Beltine" network and are listed in general order of priority of implementation.

RESTRICTED

RESTRICTED

AACS-D-353
SUBJECT: Single Side-Band Training Program

(1) Washington - Pepperrell

(2) Washington - Classified Location #1

(3) Fairfield - Elmendorf

(4) Fairfield - Okinawa

(5) Elmendorf - Okinawa

(6) (Classified Location #1) - (Classified Location #2)

(7) (Classified Location #2) - (Classified Location #3)

(8) (Classified Location #2) - Okinawa

(9) (Classified Location #3) - Okinawa

b. Sixteen (16) Single Side-Band Equipments will be made available for delivery beginning in June 1950. Several of the locations listed above will have more than one (1) equipment, depending on circuit requirements. Installation of equipment for the Washington- Pepperrell circuit is underway at this time. Three (3) airmen and one (1) officer have volunteered and have been selected for initial assignment to Fort Pepperrell as the nucleus for the first overseas installation and maintenance team.

7. Headquarters USAF has assigned this project a high priority for AACS. It naturally must have the whole-hearted support of all AACS personnel to become a reality. Since the initiation of the factory training program, the eligibility list has been reduced by discharges and other attrition factors. Accordingly, vacancies exists for applicants for this training and applications will be accepted from qualified Radio Repairmen. Applications received and approved will be given a relative priority based on recommendations as to skill and ability to absorb advanced training, plus factors governing length of service, communications experience (civilian and military), schooling and career prospects. Applications will be accepted from personnel assigned overseas as well as the Zone of Interior and must comply with current AF Regulations covering advanced technical training.

8. Assignment, classification and utilization policy:

a. Graduates of the Single Side-Band School will be considered qualified to occupy the position of Radio Repair and Maintenance Supervisor under the Career Program.

b. Assignments to stations listed in paragraph 6a will be primarily on a volunteer basis and will be scheduled sufficiently in advance

RESTRICTED

RESTRICTED

AACS-D-353
SUBJECT: Single Side-Band Training Program

to allow arrival of personnel prior to implementation of projects.

c. Graduates of the Single Side-Band course will normally be returned to their home stations to insure maximum utilization of skill pending delivery of equipment for installation.

9. Supplemental information will be forthcoming periodically on the status of this program in the AACS Technical Information Letter or by separate correspondence to all echelons of this command.

BY COMMAND OF BRIGADIER GENERAL SMITH:

/s/ Ernest S. Moon
ERNEST S. MOON
Colonel, USAF
Chief of Staff

353 1st Ind

HEADQUARTERS 1804TH AACS GROUP, APO 942, c/o Postmaster, Seattle, Washington, 25 May 1950

TO: Each Squadron & Detachment Commander, 1804th AACS Group

1. Commanders will give the Single Side-Band training program their whole-hearted support by bringing this letter to the direct and personal attention of each non-commissioned officer eligible to apply.

2. Commanders will insure that forwarding indorsements to applications contain all information possible to aid AACS in selecting only fully qualified non-commissioned officers.

BY ORDER OF COLONEL FROST:

Jack M Engle
JACK M ENGLE
Captain, USAF
Adjutant

Appendix III: Batchelor Broadband Coupler

Referring to the Figure 1 schematic, the power amplifier tube is shunt fed via RF plate choke (20). The capacity (Cp) as depicted in dotted lines represents the plate capacitance inherent in the tube's design plus any associated wiring stray capacity. Usually, this value is in the order of 20pf or less. A plate DC blocking capacitor (C) then couples high impedance signal energy into the Batchelor network (15). Consider the network as a black box, with a high impedance connection (T1), a ground refence connection (T2), and a low impedance output connection (T3). The antenna or utilization device is connected across T2 and T3 and has a typical 50 ohms impedance.

The Batchelor Network is a parallel-resonant/series-resonant one. The parallel resonant component consists of winding L1 connected in series with winding L2, both of which are connected in parallel across T1 and T2. The series combination of L1/L2 is thus in parallel with the tubes and stray capacity Cp. Since Cp is essentially a fixed, the inductive value of L1/L2 is adjusted to a point at the upper end of the desired bandpass.

Now, note windings L2/L3. These two are wound in bifilar form. L2 is a smaller number of turns than L1 and is at the "cold end" of the L1/L2 combination. Observe that between the bifilar turns of L2 and L3 there exists turn-to-turn stray capacitance. It is the result of two conductors' distance-separated by the wire's insulation. This resultant capacity,

Cs, provides for a RF coupling between the parallel-tuned portion of the network and the now series-tuned-section consisting of Cs in series with L3 and L4.

Now, for the interesting parts. The L2/L3 winding determines not only the amount of Cs capacity but also establishes the width of the desired bandpass. The series combination of L3 and L4 is adjusted for resonance at the lower bandpass breakpoint. The orientation of the L1 and L4 winding impacts the insertion loss of the network and the degree of transformer coupling between input/output sections. If the L1/L4 sections are over-coupled, the desired flat bandpass becomes double-humped (the same effect seen in over coupled IF transformers). The design goal is a flat, critically coupled response.

Several difficulties arise in designing these networks. To make them reproducible and to accommodate changes in wiring capacity (that affects L1 and L2's resonant condition), it is necessary to design to a higher bogey input capacitance and to add this to the amplifier's PA. In the 600L, this is done using what appears at first glance as a neutralizing capacitor. No, that little adjustable capacitor on the 600L band switch is there to compensate for stray capacity variation. Wes developed a keen way to neutralize the 600L's 813 final: band switching in degenerative feedback inductance into the cathode circuit.

Now, back to the RF choke (20) and the problem Tom Clemens found while building 600Ls. If the RF plate feed choke has a varying capacity versus frequency characteristic, band to band, then that capacity is added or subtracted to the target bogey value and upsets the coupler's input tuning. So, the bogey Cp value must be one that allows for small capacity variations but is not so large that coupler efficiency at 10 meter (28MHz) is adversely affected.

As one sees, designing a coupler of this type is a balancing act of many variables. The physical placement and spacing of windings, the types of insulation used, coil form material, etc. all play a role in the net output bandpass. It is easy to see why the engineering and coil teams at Central had such a difficult time in initially getting those couplers to yield....and why curious competitors who bought 600L amplifiers only to harvest couplers got nowhere, after cutting them open and disturbing wire placements.

Of course, there are other secrets to be had in this outwardly simple device—most of which are not disclosed in the patent's text. See if *you* can figure out how Wes cleverly improved 2nd harmonic rejection in Joe's groundbreaking design. Good hunting!

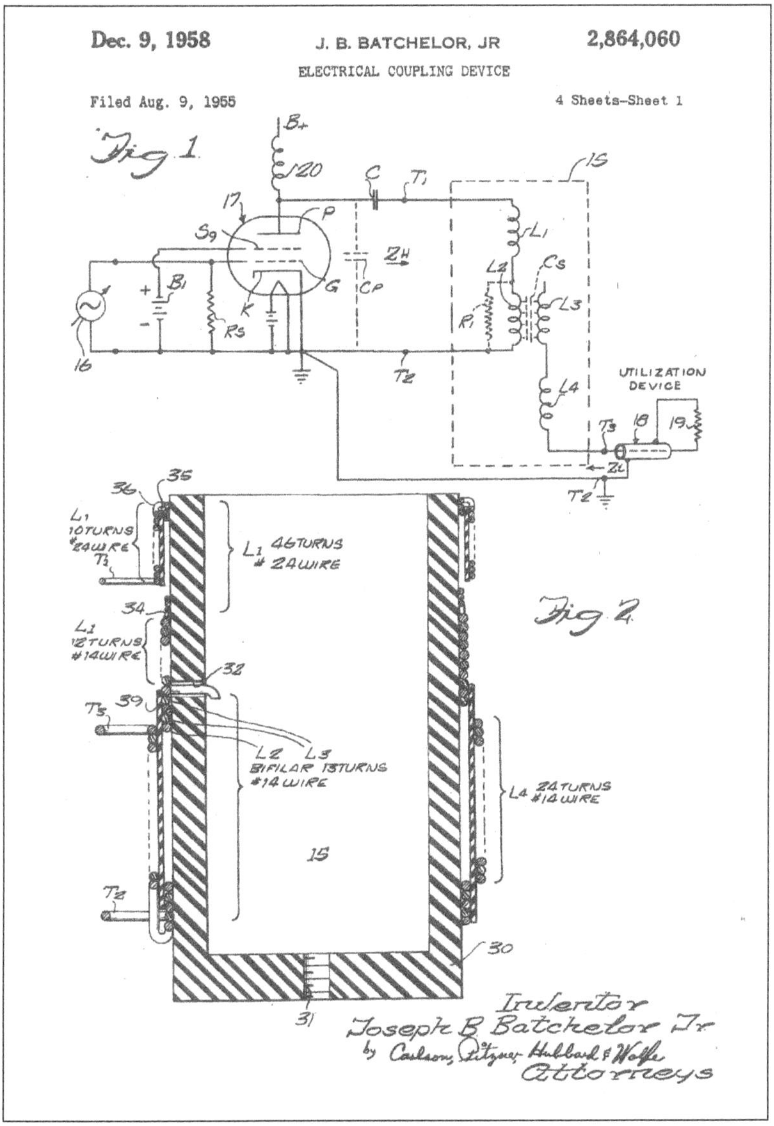

Appendix IV: CE Restoration Hints

The restoration of vintage radio equipment is a fun and rewarding endeavor, especially since any of the vintage sideband rigs from Collins, Central, Hallicrafters, National and others can hold their own, even on today's crowded amateur bands. The fundamentals behind single sideband have not changed with the years, only the manner in which equipment has evolved—from vacuum tubes to hybrids and finally all solid state. With so many different manufacturers to choose from, the collection of these fine pieces of technology truly has no bounds, except perhaps for the available space in one's ham shack.

The Central Electronics website (www.ce-multiphase.com) contains many service notes and hints on how to restore the 100V, 200V, 600L and others. What follows are ideas on how to approach restoration of this equipment, and the process you should undertake *before* applying line current for the first time.

A vintage radio restorer must be armed with technical resources. The equipment you are dealing with is decades old and is wholly different from that manufactured today. The only new equipment made today with vacuum tubes are audio amplifiers sought by audiophiles and electronic hobbyists. Fortunately, supplies of new old stock (NOS) American manufactured tubes remains strong. Numerous cottage business specializing in supplying tubes exist and are accessible via the Internet. Another good source of tubes remains the local area hamfest. Prices there are often quite reasonable, sometimes even free! But never assume every NOS tube is a good, viable tube.

Visually inspect tubes for signs of vacuum leakage. A sure sign of condition is the appearance of the getter flash. A getter is a material that is evaporated onto the tube envelope, usually at or near the top. Its purpose is to absorb gas that is emitted from tube elements when hot or that which enters the tube's envelope via leaks.

A good tube having a viable vacuum is one where the getter is a bright silvery color. If the getter has totally disappeared or has turned a milky white, you might as well discard the tube and move on. Now, assuming tubes pass the visual exam, the next step is to test them for minimum transconductance.

Tube manufacturers publish application information for tubes and you should be equipped with, minimally, receiving tubes manuals as supplied by General Electric, RCA, and Sylvania. These books provide useful information for the correct application of tubes in audio and radio frequency devices. Tube testing equipment can check tubes for emission and transconductance (an indicator of tube gain). The best tube testers can provide a transconductance test and will include information depicting the lowest level of acceptability of the average tube of a given type.

Tubes that test slightly below transconductance minimums may or may not work in a given circuit, depending upon the equipment designer's target goals. A tube that tests well below minimum should be discarded. When evaluating dual triodes, such as the 12AT7 or 12AX7 used in most all phasing exciters, it is important that the tube's two sections—particularly with respect to the two audio channels involving the audio phase shifter—have near equal transconductance characteristics. Doing so will aid you in attaining the best balance between upper and lower sideband suppression.

When reusing old tubes, always clean the envelope with a lightly moistened towel, as dirt only traps heat and hastens the demise of tubes. *Never* use shiny tube shields in vintage radio equipment, as those direct radiated heat back into tubes. The best shields are the IERC type, black in color and having heat conducting material inside the shield and contacting the tube's glass envelope.

Tubes that normally run hot such as 12BY7, 6AQ5, and 6BQ5 tubes should always have an IERC tube shield, even if a tube shield was not originally provided.

The next step in restoration should be to clean the equipment chassis and wiring thoroughly. A tidy chassis is more attractive and runs cooler. Also, the time spent in cleaning gives the restorer an opportunity to spot obviously overheated parts that must be replaced, badly installed past repairs, or modifications needing correction, as well as identification of items that are somehow now missing.

Restorers have many pet solutions to clean radios. In general, it boils down to Simple Green, Mr. Clean, household ammonia, or isopropyl alcohol. Be careful when using ammonia. I have found where a 75%/25% mixture of Mr. Clean and ammonia does an excellent job of removing dirt from Bakelite (Daka-ware) equipment knobs. You should have a large supply of wooden stick cotton swabs, as they are necessary for cleaning contacts on wafer switches. I often will first clean up a filthy wafer switch using a cotton swab soaked in lacquer thinner, then followed up with a *small* amount of DeOxit. Don't soak wafer switches with DeOxit; it only needs to be applied to actual contact surfaces, and besides, it's rather expensive. A little should go a long way.

Next, look for the electrolytic capacitors—tubular or FP-can type—and plan on replacing them all. Collins and Central made excellent radio equipment, but neither firm was in the electrolytic capacitor business. NOS FP-capacitors often can be reformed but be very careful when doing so. *Do not* try to use the rig's power supply to reform anything! That's a great way to kill a power transformer. Either buy a commercial capacitor analyzer (i.e., Sprague Tel-Ohmike) that includes a metered leakage indicator, or build one.

Today's axial leaded capacitors are available at higher temperature rating than those originally used in vintage gear. A 105-degree unit is preferred, as tube gear runs hot. Newly-manufactured, domestic FP-style capacitors can be purchased from either Hayseed Hamfest or CE-Distribution.

Paper tubular capacitors (the type coated in wax or a hard Bakelite cover) are usually leaky and should be replaced with modern film type equivalents. Tubes usually die not of old age but from being over-stressed, with capacitors being the A #1 cause of such failures. I have restored 100V and 200V transmitters that still have their original final amplifier tubes, so please don't suggest that vacuum tubes are unreliable! Aside from capacitors, the next biggest killer of tubes is excessive line voltage, which translate to excessive filament voltage.

Tubes used in vintage radios have either a 6.3 or 12.6 filament rating. Having the filament voltage a bit low by a few percentage points is not so bad, but being high by 5 or 10% will result in lots of tubes that are dead before their time. Many operators of vintage gear install bucking transformers to lower AC line voltage to the design level radio engineers used in the 1940s–'50s, 115VAC. Many homes today see line voltages as high as 128 volts, which will silently kill vacuum tubes.

A few useful hints now for all CE exciters... The original diodes used in the various balanced modulators are now beginning to fail. A great replacement for those early point-contact types is a Schottky diode, and the type I've used is 1N5711. Fifty of them—a lifetime supply, for many restorers—will typically run about $10.00.

When rebuilding 100V and 200V exciters, you must change out *all* the Chemtronics axial leaded electrolytic capacitors. They are easy to spot, since they have white ceramic outer tubes (that will usually be cracked) and bright red end caps. There is one hiding around the balanced modulator potentiometers that many restorers overlook. Also, there is one in the PA cage that shunts the screen relay's coil. I strongly recommend axial leaded tantalum capacitors here, as they are more stable than the typical electrolytic type. Buy from a reputable supplier, such as Sprague/Vishay or Kemet.

The fan motors can be easily rebuilt. Their normal problem is either gummy lubricant and/or a worn-out endplay washer. A fiber washer from your local electronics house or via the Internet should do the trick. A good material to clean out old gummy oil is Ronson lighter fluid, available at many drug stores.

The PS-2 phase shift network is a normally reliable unit except for two mica capacitors: C128 (1850.4pf) and C130 (4711.2pf). Note that each has impressed plate voltage from the preceding audio phase inverter's 12AT7. Those mica capacitors develop sporadic leakage at times, which then applies some level of positive leakage voltage to the grids of the next AF amplifier stage, thereby killing the set's sideband suppression.

These exact value capacitors are obviously not available from suppliers, and so you will have to fashion a replacement by measuring a batch of micas to find some that closely match up. Fortunately, the leakage does not appear to inhibit measuring the "leaky" capacitor's value on a capacitance meter. So, the selection of a replacement group then merely requires matching that indicated value. Some have suggested adding a 1uF series blocking capacitor and thereby isolate plate voltage from those two vulnerable micas; however, that really doesn't fix the problem that the micas are gradually failing.

Prior to adjusting the AF ratio, AF balance, and the two RF phase shift coils for best sideband suppression, attach an oscilloscope (x10 probe) to the secondary (point B) of the 8MC oscillator plate coil and adjust for maximum 8MHz level. The 100V/200V manual provides methods for sideband suppression adjustments; however, the easiest and best method is visually via a spectrum analyzer. The four adjustments do interact, so you will have to gradually vary them each to achieve best sideband suppression. Once adjusted, the system is very stable; suppression will remain in balance for very long periods of time.

If, while performing the sweep adjustments of the various bandpass couplers, the gain of a stage is low or an adjustment seems to do little to nothing, you may have a cracked tuning slug. Inspect and replace if necessary.

When replacing final amplifier tubes, the only newly manufactured tubes worth considering are the Russian Tung-Sol branded 6550s. Do not bother with the Chinese variety; while they appear to work for most audio applications, their gain is poor on 15 and 10 meters.

When powering up a newly rebuilt rig for the first time, do not just plug it in, hit the switch, and wait for sparks or smoke. Blown fuses and sparks happen for a reason, usually a hard short circuit due to a wiring error. Invest in a metered Variac, one that indicates applied voltage *and* drawn current. These can be found on eBay or can be a nice weekend project to build at home.

Plug everything up, set the Variac to zero-volts, and turn the rig on. *Slowly* increase the applied voltage while watching the current draw. If you see the current rising very quickly, STOP. You likely have a short circuit or improperly installed part somewhere. Resolve that problem and try again. In a properly configured 100V, the indicated line current in the standby mode should be approximately 2.5 amperes. It will be slightly less for a 200V, since it uses solid state rectifiers (no tube rectifier heaters).

Do not substitute solid state rectifiers for the tube ones in the 100V. While tubes do produce heat, they are kind to the filter capacitors by slowly ramping up the applied rectified voltage. This 'feature' has materially enhanced 100V capacitor survivability. The 100V's rectifier heat shield does an effective job of isolating the three B+ capacitors from excessively high radiated heat via the three rectifier tubes. I have replaced far more HV filter capacitors in 200V transmitters as compared to 100Vs, no doubt due to high initial surge currents. When you turn on a 200V, there is no gradual rectified voltage buildup. In those sets, power is fully applied in one 60Hz cycle to the discharged capacitors...and after 50 years, they really don't appreciate it!

Also, keep in mind that the high vacuum rectifier tubes in the 100V have an approximate 30 volt drop, which if replaced by silicon will result in much higher applied B+ voltages.

Another item to look out for is the OA2 regulator tube. Just because it is glowing doesn't mean it's sinking the set's required current. When conducting, the 0A2 places some load on the low-voltage power supply, which is already running high due to elevated line voltage. If the OA2 is worn out, the applied B+ voltage may exceed the filter capacitor's 450v rating and lead to an eventual failure.

Once you get through the power up stage of a freshly rebuilt radio, you should proceed with the alignment process described by the manufacturer. If a stage has abnormally low gain or seems to be dead, and the set's various coil/capacitors adjustments have not been obviously tampered with, then start doing voltage level measurements for the stages in question. Keep in mind, alignment never fixes bad components or faulty wiring.

Don't be shocked to find an occasionally unsoldered solder joint, missed from the factory. It happens to all manufacturers, even Collins. When new and the wires and ties points were shinny clean, a tightly cinched component connection will often work without solder, and for some years in many cases. Just chalk it up to being human, fix it now, and move on.

As you progress in the restoration hobby and find yourself consumed with finding new radios to rebuild, don't be too alarmed. Boatanchor restoration is one of those sub-hobbies of amateur radio that leads to many other things, such as homebrewing new radios using tubes or developing useful modification enhancements to vintage gear. That's all good stuff and is highly encouraged!

In time, you will need to add to your stockpile of restoration tools. I'm not talking about signal generators or spectrum analyzers, as everyone gradually adds those to the workshop. The tools I mean are those that help make an average restoration look great. Nothing detracts more from any project than chipped, faded paint, rusty hardware, or dinged knobs and escutcheons.

You will need some tools that might seem odd for an electronic shop: a wheel-type metal polisher, a bead blaster cabinet, spray painting gun assortment, and a viable air compressor/air dryer system. A floor or desktop mounted polisher is great for restoring Bakelite knobs and other small parts to better-than-new beauty. Red jeweler's rouge and a couple of cotton polishing mitts can make what were once dull, rough looking knobs into those that speak high quality.

The one piece of equipment that is as indispensable as a Tektronix oscilloscope is a bead blasting cabinet. I know that sounds odd, but the first step to refinishing rusty parts of any type and getting panels stripped and ready for painting is via a bead blaster and glass beads. The glass beads will make quick work of surface rust on items such as transformer bell covers or cabinets. The after effect is a perfectly clean, very slightly etched surface that provides an excellent means for primer or paint adhesion.

It doesn't have to have a huge cabinet; we're not detailing cylinder heads. Mine is the smaller side-loading cabinet Model SC-35V sold by Tip Tools and Equipment. What this device does is make you forget all about chemical strippers, wire brushes, or sandpaper. A good bead blaster cabinet will make what took hours of hard, sweaty work now a job done in minutes. Don't overlook Craigslist as a local source for used bead blasters; that's where mine came from, and the cost was a fair $200.

Inexpensive spray paint guns are available from Harbor Freight and will do an exceptional job. Having two guns allows one for priming and the other for finish work. Of course, even better finishes are possible with high end guns made by DeVilbiss and others. Often these can be found on the used market and are highly desirable.

It used to be difficult to buy paint in the appropriate "boatanchor" colors, but computer paint matching has made that a non-issue. I use acrylic enamel paint sourced from local paint stores that cater to automobile body shops. Adding a hardener additive will make that paint resistant to scratches, far better than any rattle can. I've found the counter people at these auto paint stores to be highly knowledgeable, and when you explain that what you're painting isn't an automobile, you'd be surprised at how many useful hints they are willing to share.

One last item the heavy-duty boatanchor restorer should consider is a used electric oven. If you intend to speed up the drying time for paints and want to get a rock-hard finish, an electric oven set for 150–170 degrees is what you need. *Do not* put your painted items in the kitchen oven. Your finished product might come out great, but the XYL will make certain you don't live to tell the story. Check with Craigslist, as used but good ones can often be had for a song...$75 or so.

Wrinkle finish painting looks great, but the choices of color boils down to black, gray and red. No boatanchor guy will likely ever need red wrinkle paint, but the other two colors are obvious choices to keep in stock. Keep in mind, the gray wrinkle can get you the desired texture, and then a light overspray coat of the desired color can get you to the finish line. I've found the VHT series of wrinkle paints to be the best *but make sure to follow the application instructions exactly*: left to right, right to left, and then across and back at a 45-degree angle. Once done, place the painted item into your preheated oven and come back in 30 minutes to a beautifully wrinkled finish.

I've done this for years and have never once been disappointed.

Finally, here is a tip that was passed along by a fellow restorer that bears repeating. Thit hint is for the Collins guys who have nasty, orange-colored S-line trim rings or for anyone who is restoring older plastic-encased electronic/computer items that have gradually faded from pristine white to—well, you know. It is possible to restore these to like new condition chemically. The best part is that the chemical needed is conveniently premixed, very inexpensive, and is available at beauty supply houses just about everywhere. It is called Salon Care 40 Volume Crème Developer, and is stocked by Sally Beauty Supply, LLC. If I can find it in little Covington, Louisiana, it is truly available *anywhere*. A 32 oz container costs a whopping $6.49.

You need a large clear plastic bag, a foam-type paint brush, and this gel-like hair conditioner. Simply lather it all over the trim ring. Don't be stingy; really pile it on. Place the coated trim ring into the plastic bag, zip it up, and leave out in the bright sun for a day (or for faster results under an ultraviolet lamp). Clean with fresh water and see if the plastic is white enough for your taste. If not, give it a second treatment.

One 32 oz container should do the typical Collins 75S, 32S-3, 312B4, and 30L-1 combination. Not bad for a few bucks and some free sunlight!

Of course, this trick does not work for the earlier metal trim rings used on Collin gear. There one must carefully sand and repaint the trim ring to complement their restoration's handiwork. Surplus Sales of Nebraska is one source for Collins paint, stocked in handy rattle-style spray cans.

Appendix V: Definitions

Ampere (A): A unit measurement of electrical current

Amplitude: The height of an electronic or physical wave from an average or median position

AM: Amplitude modulation

Amplifier: An electronic device used to increase voltage, current or power

Antenna: A device to either radiate radio signals from a transmitter, or to receive signals from a distant radio source

ARRL: The American Radio Relay League, the national ham radio association in the USA

AVC: Automatic volume control, as used in radio receivers

Base station: A radio station located at a fixed location

Bandpass filter: An electronic network designed to pass a certain range of frequencies

Band: That portion of the electromagnetic spectrum allocated to amateur, commercial, military, aviation, or maritime radio operations

BFO (beat frequency oscillator): An oscillator circuit that mixes its output with an incoming radio signal to produce an audio frequency tone for CW reception. In SSB operation, the beat frequency oscillator in a radio receiver replaces the carrier, which was suppressed when the signal was originally transmitted.

Boatanchor: An expression used to describe vacuum tube radio equipment

Buffer amplifier: An amplifier usually following an oscillator to reduce loading/frequency pulling effects

Callsign: A unique identifier for each radio amateur and licensed radio station throughout the world. In the USA, callsigns are granted by the Federal Communications Commission.

Capacitor: A passive electronic component composed of two conducting plates separated by a dielectric insulating material

Carrier frequency: The center frequency of a radio signal

Carrier power: The average power supplied to the antenna by an unmodulated transmitter

Coaxial cable (coax): A signal transmission line that has a central conductor and an outer shield

Conductor: A material through which electricity easily flows

CQ: Request for radio contact, "calling any operator"

CQ magazine: An amateur radio publication by CQ Communications.

CW: Continuous wave

dB (decibel): The numerical ratio of two power measurements

DXpedition: An expedition by radio amateurs to locations that may be geographically or physically remote, and from where amateur contacts are rare

Electron tube (AKA vacuum tube): A device that modifies an electrical signal through the movement of electrons in a vacuum. Types include, diodes, triodes, tetrodes, and pentodes, each having two, three four or five internal elements, respectively.

Elmer: Slang for a person who helps newcomers get started in amateur radio

FCC (Federal Communications Commission): The US government body that regulates the use of the radio spectrum.

Filter: An electric circuit, often called a network, that allows certain frequencies to pass but rejects/attenuates others

FM (frequency modulation): A means of adding voice intelligence to a carrier signal by changing its instantaneous frequency in direct proportion to the instantaneous amplitude of an input signal, often human speech

Frequency: The number of complete waves or cycles that pass a reference point per second, expressed in hertz (Hz)

Fuse: A circuit protection device that self-destructs when excessive electric current passes through it for a given period of time

GHz (gigahertz): One billion Hertz (1 000 000 000 Hz) or cycles.

Ground-plane antenna: A quarter wavelength signal radiator having radials extending horizontally from its base

Hz (hertz): A unit of measure for frequency

Heterodyne: The resultant radio signal after mixing two different-frequency signals together.

HF (high frequency): Radio signal energy in the range of 3MHz to 30MHz

Homebrew: Homebuilt equipment

IF (intermediate frequency): A different frequency at which radio signals are amplified and processed internally within a receiver

Ionosphere: A region in the atmosphere containing ionized gasses that refract (bend) radio waves and direct them back toward earth. The ionosphere is what permits HF radio signals to span great distances, well beyond line of sight.

Inductor: a coil of wire, often used with capacitors to form tuned circuits for use as filters, within oscillators, and as ripple filters in power supplies

Interference: The undesired interaction between two or more radio frequencies

Intermodulation: The undesired mixing of two or more frequencies, producing undesirable and potentially interfering additional frequencies

Insulator: A substance through which electricity does not pass easily

Key: A simple mechanical device (switch) used to send Morse code

kHz (kilohertz): One thousand hertz (Hz), or one thousand cycles per second

LSB: Lower sideband

MHz (megahertz): One million hertz (HZ), or one million cycles per second

Microphone: A device that converts sound energy into electrical signals

Microwave: Radio signals above 1GHz in frequency

Modulation: The process of adding information to a carrier wave

Modulator: The device that adds information to a carrier wave

Morse code: The mechanically coded process used by radio operators instead of voice communications.

NBFM: Narrowband frequency modulation

Negative feedback: A process by which a portion of an amplifier's output is returned to the input, 180 degrees out of phase

Net: A scheduled and pre-structured on-air meeting of radio operators

Noise: Unwanted electromagnetic energy that interferes with signal transmission or reception

Ohm: The electrical unit for resistance

OM (old man): Any male operator, regardless of age or marital status.

Oscillator: A device that produces an electrical signal at a particular frequency

Power: The rate of electrical energy consumption, calculated by multiplying voltage by current (amperes)

Propagation: The physical means for transferring radio energy between other points/locations

PTT: Push to talk

QRM: Q code for man-made noise or interference to radio signals.

QRP: Q code used to request or suggest low power operations, usually understood to mean transmitted power at or below 5 watts.

QSB: Code describing the effect of fading of radio signals.

QTH: Home location of radio station

Quartz crystal: A sliced section silicon dioxide cut or ground to vibrate at a particular frequency when an electric current is applied to its edges; used as frequency determining devices in transmitters and receivers and also in certain bandpass filters

Regulator: A electronic device which maintains a constant output voltage or current over a range of load currents and input voltages

Resistance: The measure of how much an object or material opposes the flow of an electric current

Resistor: A device that opposes the flow of electric current

RF (radio frequencies): Electromagnetic energy that can pass through space

S/N (signal to noise ratio): The measurable proportion of signal power to noise power. The better the S/N ratio, the better the quality of the signal, and the easier it is to recover intelligence information

Skip: A radio phenomenon in which radio signals are reflected or refracted by the ionosphere and return to earth in unexpected places

Sporadic E-skip: Unexpected and unpredictable propagation due to refraction in the ionosphere's E layer, approximately 150 miles above the Earth's surface

SSB (single sideband): A special form of amplitude modulation that occupies one-half the bandwidth of normal double sideband and carrier transmitted signal

SSSC (single sideband suppressed carrier): An early name for SSB

Sunspot: A region on the sun where an electromagnetic eruption of energy is occurring. These have both positive and negative effects on radio signal propagation

Transmission Line: Another term for antenna feedline

UHF (ultra-high frequency): Radio energy in the range 300MHz to 3,000MHz

USB: Upper sideband

uV: Microvolt, or one-millionth of a volt.

Volt: The unit of electric potential difference between two points

Vacuum tube: See electron tube

VFO: Variable frequency oscillator

VHF (very high frequency): Radio energy in the range of 30MHz to 300MHz

VOX: Voice operated transmit

Waveguide: A hollow transmission line, typically square or rectangular in cross-section, used to carry microwave signals

Wavelength: The distance in meters (or feet) between corresponding points on a wave

XYL: Abbreviation for wife of an amateur radio operator

YL (young lady): Abbreviation for young lady, any female radio operator regardless of age or marital status

Zero beat: A process whereby one or both of two signals are adjusted in frequency so that they are identical and in phase

Appendix VI: Citations/References

The principal source material used in this book include private papers, interviews, photographs and product documentation as provided by the Schum family. In addition, the work includes information contained within private recorded conversations and mail correspondence between the author and Wes Schum, Joseph Batchelor, and Tom Clemens.

Information describing the history of single sideband pertaining to amateur radio's experimentation with the technology between years 1947 and 1962 is sourced from published editorial, letters to the editor, and article information as contained in *QST Magazine* and *CQ Magazine*. Specific citations are so noted in this book.

Material and photographs pertaining to the American Television Institute (formerly located in Chicago, Illinois) and its founder, U. A. Sanabria have been provided by the Early Television Foundation and Museum (www.earlytelevision.org).

Appendix VII: End Note Stories/ Interviews

Observations from Andy Calandria, K5MVP:

It was October 1957 in New Orleans, Louisiana that an anxiously anticipated little white envelope from the FCC was waiting for me to open. I had received a Novice Class license, which was amateur radio's beginners license that was good for a scant one year, with the call sign KN5MVP. The N in my call sign indicated to others I was a beginning Ham operator. A year later I passed the General Class test, becoming K5MVP.

The General Class license meant I was able to operate on the voice-bands using amplitude modulation, also called AM. The voice or phones bands were very crowded then, and you heard lots of heterodynes. A heterodyne is when two AM stations are too close together, causing a loud, annoying interference tone. After a few months on AM phone, I began to hear many AM stations complaining about "slop buckets." I had no earthly idea what they were talking about, but after a while I learned that in certain parts of the amateur bands, there were amateurs operating a very new mode of voice communication called single sideband, or SSB.

I tuned to the part of the band where these SSB stations operated, but could not understand anything they were saying. I then understood why the AM stations called them slop buckets; they sounded like a bunch of screeching pigs! Eventually, I soon learned how to tune SSB properly and began hearing voices. You see, AM (amplitude modulation) has a carrier wave, and that carrier contains no voiced modulation until you attach an audio amplifier, or modulator, to the transmitter; then people can hear and understand you. You see, AM has two identical voice-carrying sidebands, a lower and upper, on either side of the carrier signal. The carrier is the frequency part of the signal and is later used in AM-capable receivers by making the sidebands understandable.

Here is where SSB runs circles around AM: You only need *one* sideband to convey voice information. With SSB, you eliminate the carrier and one of the two sidebands; now you have 100% of your transmitter's power concentrated in just one sideband. But wait, I just said you need a carrier signal to understand amplitude modulated audio, but with SSB you have eliminated the carrier. The one voiceband of SSB, either lower or upper sideband, is now the sole radio signal containing voice information, but you still need a carrier to not make it sound like a slop bucket, as the AM stations called SSB. Now what?

In all communication receivers there is a circuit called the BFO, the beat frequency oscillator. This BFO is what generates a carrier signal *in the receiver*, thus replacing the transmitter's missing carrier. Now you can understand SSB, and by eliminating the extra sideband and the carrier you have made SSB a very efficient mode of communication, far overpowering traditional AM.

From what I experienced and heard on-air, it took many years for SSB to overtake AM, but as more and more amateurs saw how efficient SSB was and learned how to tune it, the writing was on the wall for AM. By the late 1960s, the term *slop bucket* faded into the sunset along with widespread use of AM, as by then SSB reigned supreme for HF voice communications.

How David Beckler, N0SAP Became a Ham:

My uncle, Charles Anderson of New Orleans, worked at Avondale Shipyards as an electrician. He also repaired tabletop radios in his garage as a hobby, and I would visit him in the garage at times. He taught me simple electronics, then gave me a Philco AM/SW radio to take home.

With a simple antenna wire connected to the back of an electrically-hot chassis and no cabinet, I tuned the airwaves every night searching for strong signals from overseas. Somehow, I didn't electrocute myself! It was not long before my simple receiver mash-up stumbled across some guys talking about radios. I would tune in and eavesdrop on them almost every night.

Telling my uncle of my find, he said, "Those are hams, amateur radio operators. You should look into that and get licensed so you can do the same." Even though my uncle was not a ham, his encouragement pushed me into this wonderful hobby.

I will never forget this one callsign from that overheard crowd. He would say, "This is W4AOE: We're Four America's Oldest Eagle." He seemed to be a grumpy old man, always talking about SSB vs AM and why SSB was no good. "This single sideband stuff is just going to ruin ham radio. There is nothing better than the pure modulation of AM radio." Somehow his comments stuck in my head after all these years...maybe because he pounded on the same message, night after night!

I decided on amateur radio because of the challenge to learn Morse Code, which was necessary to get an FCC license. I learned Morse Code by sounding out each letter with my mouth from the family encyclopedia. Gradually I learned A to Z, then the numbers, and after some time, added punctuation like the period, comma, and a few other. It was not until two weeks before taking my Novice test that I bought a Hallicrafters S-108, only to hear the tones of Morse Code for the first time.

I passed my Novice test and almost eight weeks later received an official letter from the FCC containing my callsign, WN5SAP. I thought, *SAP? What is the FCC doing to me?!* The club members thought it was a great callsign, which made me think, *Hey, maybe this is something special.* I have been "The SAP" ever since, but after several relocations, I am now known in Nixa (Missouri) as NØSAP or N0-SAP. No matter, as this is my radio name I go by every day on every mode, CW, SSB, or AM. Today, if you call me David, I may not even turn around.

There are many stories from my life, spanning from childhood to present day--of building radios and antennas, undertaking experiments that worked or failed. The ones that failed only made me a better ham by learning what went wrong. Those so-called failures were an invaluable learning tool I use to this day in improving my own station, as well as while helping other hams.

I still enjoy the thrill of CW, SSB, and AM contacts. I am not a digital dude, so don't plan to hear me on FT-8 anytime soon. I like *real* radios: those with high voltage and vacuum tubes. "Make them glow in the dark and spark!" There is nothing else like it. Happy hamming.

AM vs SSB Wars: Dr. Bob Heil, K9EID

The late to mid-1950s brought interesting times to amateur radio. The number of licensed amateur radio operators was growing by leaps and bounds. In 1951 Wes Schum, W9DYV, had entered this growing market with a new mode of transmission called single sideband. Wes had a very interesting way of introducing the mode by visiting hamfests, demonstrating the many qualities of this new mode. His original transmitters were kits that one could buy and build to join this great new mode. His first transmitter, the Central Electronics 10A, produced no carrier and only one sideband. His thought was the SSB signal would be much narrower in bandwidth (only 2.5kHz to 3.0 kHz, versus the 8kHz to 9kHz for AM) and allow for more signals on the air simultaneously.

As this new mode of SSB was growing in popularity, it was beginning to brush against aggravation and negative thoughts from the more predominant AM operators. AM took up much more bandwidth, and this new SSB mode was the answer to the problem of how to accommodate far more stations on the limited amateur radio bands. Several other manufactures followed Wes in his quest to bring SSB to amateur radio's airwaves, thus causing more and more SSB activity. In 1955, Art Collins made the major announcement that his company, Collins Radio, was abandoning production of AM equipment; in 1957, Collins introduced its first SSB transceiver, the KWM-1. The reviews were simply glowing for this first SSB transceiver. It was an instant hit.

Along with all of this new activity by a fast-growing number of licensed operators, coupled with the increased usage of the new SSB mode, the airwaves began to experience disgruntled AM operators who were very defiant of SSBs operators. In step, SSB operators were not pleased by the spectrum-hogging bandwidth of AM signals, or what they viewed as obnoxious operating practices. For several years this shared animosity grew and grew, eventually to the point of serious consequences. Battle lines were being drawn.

I was licensed in 1956 and within two years had built a Central Electronics 10B, soon followed by a 20A—both of which I purchased as kits. Kit-building was fun, and I enjoyed being able to operate a transmitter that I had built myself, one that Wes Schum had designed so well and made so easy for a new operator to enjoy.

The story goes that within two weeks on the air with my Harvey Wells transmitter on six meters in September of 1956, I ran across a SSB signal on six meters! WHAT? SSB was really prominent on 75 or 40 meters at that time, but had not made it to VHF. I began meeting that fellow each night as he adjusted his new 6-meter sideband transmitter, which he had built using a Central Electronics 10B as the foundation. Over the next year Larry Burrows, K0DGE and chief engineer at KMOX-CBS radio in St Louis, guided me through the building of my own 10B kit and his unique conversion to operate it on 6 meters. I followed that with building a Johnson Viking 6 and 2 meter Thunderbolt 1,000-watt amplifier.

Yes, I became the big signal on the block, on 6 and 2 meter sideband.

During all of this, I would listen on 75 meters occasionally, and started hearing some very interesting, very heated conversations among powerful AM stations that wanted no part of these new SSB stations encroaching on their territory. Those heated conversations grew to be very radical as time passed. Before long, 75 meters became an AM-SSB war zone.

In time, things became violent. Horrible accusations were tossed about between several of the ringleaders. One evening, I was listening as one of the sideband stations related how matters were getting out of hand. He had answered a heavy knock on his front door one night only to find a rugged-looking gentleman with a shotgun in his hand, proclaiming that this was a warning. He didn't want to hear any more of that slop bucket stuff anywhere near *his* frequency—or else.

Clearly, things were spinning totally out of control between the AM operators and the sidebanders. A week or so later, I overheard another on-air conversation relating a similar story, only in that case the visitor had an ax in hand! All of this was in the winter of 1960. And these were not isolated incidents, but were fast becoming everyday occurrences.

The culmination of this (and oddly the cure for it all) was a plan for some of these groups to meet at the Dayton Hamvention and sort out their differences. I wasn't there, nor did I hear of any fighting or hot-headed arguments. No doubt, temperatures were high—but what it did precipitate was the two diverse groups agreeing to a compromise. In what they called a "Gentlemen's Agreement," the warring parties agreed that 3870kHz to 3890kHz on 75 meters, and 7285kHz to 7895kHz on the 40-meter band, would be reserved for AM operations. These frequencies were chosen as most AM transmitters were crystal controlled and could not easily move about, whereas the new sideband transmitters were controlled by VFO.

Things calmed down pretty quickly, but there were some operators who did not completely adhere to this new Gentlemen's Agreement. To most, it seemed like the Agreement would be the best, most viable solution. Peace and tranquility between the two voice modes existed for a couple of decades, but as new operators came on the air in the 1980s and beyond, it became clear they did not know of the Agreement. It was not widely publicized, so the airwaves began heating up a bit until the ARRL and many local clubs and interested parties began reasserting the Agreement to get everyone's attention.

As we are now into the next century, AM has seen a renaissance with many new operators discovering the fun of restoring and operating vintage radio equipment. Thus, a growing number of operators are now enjoying the fruits of AM, while paying attention to their neighboring SSB friends

Acknowledgments

In my wildest dreams, while studying electrical engineering and working to become an expert in my craft, not once did I envision authoring a book. So, when embarking on this new adventure—writing about my wonderful mentor and Ham radio friend, Wes Schum—it didn't take long to figure this journey would require an extensive team effort. Fortunately for me, the big collaborator in this was endeavor Wes himself. Anyone who knew Wes would understand that he never, ever threw any documents or notes away. His mountain load of 'engineer debris' became a treasure trove of information—much of which you will read here. Over our many years, an occasional unannounced Wes-shipment of Central Electronics treasures would arrive at my front door. In my mind's eye I could see that big 10-kilowatt grin of his—knowing that his treasures would be safe with me.

I am so fortunate to have been virtually adopted by the Schum family and, more importantly by Diane (Schum) Vogt and her husband, John. Whenever I asked for obscure images or items I knew existed somewhere, somehow those two would find them in short order.

The best advice Diane passed on was the name of an excellent manuscript editor that could help guide my early drafts into a fun, entertaining read. Judi Hopson and her assistant, Shanna Light, answered every question this new author could lob over the fence. Yet, a finished manuscript doesn't print itself. Here, Judi had the answer and an important referral—Janie Jessie and her team at Jan-Carol Publishing. When stepping into a new field, such as book writing, new authors are typically wary of making time-eating, costly mistakes. While I clearly didn't know what I didn't know, and often couldn't ask the right questions, Janie and Shanna answered every obscure publishing question, charted a steady course, and their publishing and editing expertise made this book a reality.

Of course, my fellow vintage radio collectors who kept asking more questions about Wes and his Central Electronics products deserve mention. Their questions, encouragement, and enthusiasm ignited the need to tell Wes Schum's story. A special thanks goes to Bob Sullivan W0YVA and Bob Heil K9EID. As I wrote each chapter, those two advance editors gave invaluable insight and focus as Wes' story gradually came to life.

Finally, where would I be without my wonderful wife, Elizabeth. You were always in my corner—even when I was more than a bit ornery. Without your enthusiastic support and encouragement, this story would still be held hostage in my mind.

About the Author

Dominic (Nick) Tusa is a principal radio communications consultant and founder of Tusa Consulting Services. For over 42 years, Tusa has provided technical services involving the design, implementation, and maintenance of land mobile radio and microwave communication systems for both public safety and private industry.

Tusa earned his first Amateur Radio license at age 11 and has been continuously active in the hobby for 57 years. He received his electrical engineering degree from Tulane University in 1975 and holds both FCC Amateur Extra Class (K5EF) and General Radio Telephone Licenses. Tusa can be reached via email at nick.tusa@ce-multiphase.com.

Lightning Source UK Ltd.
Milton Keynes UK
UKHW011842110522
402841UK00005B/1194